The Beats

Park Honan was born in New York in 1928, attended Deep Springs College, California, and took his MA at Chicago University. As a student he sat in Nelson Algren's writing course, and worked in summer jobs in the far west. After completing his Ph. D at London University, he taught literature at various universities, including Brown and Birmingham University, and he has often lectured on the Beat writers of the 1950s and 1960s.

His books include *Browning's Characters*, *The Book, the Ring, and the Poet* (with William Irvine), a biography of Matthew Arnold and a life of Jane Austen (forthcoming). Twice a Guggenheim Fellow, he is now Professor of English and American Literature at the University of Leeds.

D1452412

EF.

THE BEATS

An Anthology of 'Beat' Writing

Edited by Park Honan

J. M. Dent & Sons Ltd
London Melbourne

This selection first published in Great Britain by J. M. Dent & Sons
Ltd 1987
Introduction, selection, Further Reading list and Biographical Notes
© Park Honan 1987
The copyright information on the Acknowledgements pages constitutes
an extension to this copyright notice.

This book is Phototypeset in Linotron 10½/12pt Caledonia by Input
Typesetting Ltd, London SW19 8DR

Printed in Great Britain by Cox & Wyman Ltd, Reading
for J. M. Dent & Sons Ltd
Aldine House, 33 Welbeck Street, London W1M 8LX

British Library Cataloguing in Publication Data

The Beats.—(Everyman fiction)
  1. American literature—20th century
  I. Honan, Park
  810.8′0054   PS535.5

ISBN 0–460–02499–X

CONTENTS

CONTENTS

INTRODUCTION

Eisenhower, two Columbia University students, and the origins of the 'Beat' movement

Slim, bearded, with slightly staring eyes but a pleasant face, Allen Ginsberg stood up in a San Francisco gallery in October 1955 to read 'Howl'. This was the beginning of the 'Beat' movement in American literature. The poet had been a wayward Columbia University student, but his poem was to be as famous as any since T. S. Eliot's *The Waste Land*.

England has often been more hospitable than America to twentieth-century American poetry (Robert Frost printed his first two volumes here), and the first edition of 'Howl' was printed in England by Villiers, passed through US Customs and published late in 1956 by City Lights Bookstore, in San Francisco. However, Customs seized 520 copies of the second printing on 25 March 1957, and on 3 April the American Civil Liberties Union decided to contest the legality of the seizure since it considered the poem not obscene. A California court finally agreed 'Howl' had cultural value and meanwhile interest in the obscenity trial made Ginsberg and the 'Beats' famous.

A few months later, when Jack Kerouac's novel *On the Road* was published by Viking Press in New York on September 5, interest in the Beats became frenzied, and Jack Kerouac was made to explain to the press or TV what 'Beat' meant. He remembered Herbert Huncke of Chicago saying 'Man, I'm beat'—and 'I knew right away what he meant somehow', said Jack; but the word had the connotation of *upbeat*, and also, as Kerouac insisted, of *beatific*. '*Beat* is really saying *beatific*, see?' To one TV-interviewer who asked what he was looking for, Kerouac replied that he was waiting to see the face of God. With his enthusiasm for Thelonius Monk and Charlie Parker, he also insisted the word had a relation to jazz and bop. 'And so Huncke appeared to us and said "I'm beat" with radiant light shining out of his despairing eyes.' It was a word, Kerouac admitted, 'perhaps brought from some midwest carnival or junk cafeteria. It was a new language, actually spade [Negro] jargon but you soon learned it.' In 1948 John Clellon Holmes had prodded him to characterize his attitude and Kerouac had spoken then of young hipsters at Times Square walking down the street, watchful, catlike, in the street but not of it, and he felt the hipsters expressed his own and his generation's 'beatness—I mean, being right down to it, to ourselves, because we *really* know where we are—and a weariness with all the forms, all the conventions of the world . . . . It's something like that. So I guess you might say we're a *beat* generation.' Holmes had picked up the term in writing 'This is the Beat Generation' for *The New York Times* in 1952, and so the media had the word 'Beat' to conjure with five years later when Ginsberg and Kerouac were being interviewed.

What had influenced Ginsberg and Kerouac?

Both young men at the university in upper Manhattan had known two of the finest professors alive, Lionel Trilling and Mark Van Doren. A subtle, questing liberal humanist in the tradition of Matthew Arnold (the subject of his first book), Trilling in the 1940s was arguably the most skilful literary critic in America. He was touched and bewildered to have among his students a young Jewish homosexual, Allen Ginsberg, who struck up a personal relationship with him: Ginsberg would show his poems to Trilling, ask for advice and boast of antics. Lionel and Diana Trilling as Jews were shocked and mystified, for example, when Allen got into trouble with the Dean by writing 'Fuck the Jews' on his Hamilton Hall window. Allen claimed his cleaning-lady disliked Jews, and he'd hoped the phrase would get his window cleaned. Columbia's Dean was not amused; nor were the Trillings.

Even odder than Allen Ginsberg of New Jersey (where he was born in 1926) was his lover, confederate, and fellow writer Jack Kerouac, a handsome young man born in 1922 at Lowell, Massachusetts to parents with French-Canadian roots in Quebec. Kerouac came to Columbia before the war on an athletic scholarship, drifted back, and was conceded to be the best student in Professor Mark Van Doren's Shakespeare course. Van Doren gave him an 'A', listened to him, read his typescripts and told Harcourt Brace to publish his novel, *The*

Town and the City, but was horrified to find Kerouac banned from campus after his arrest as a material witness to a murder. Even so, when an official burst into Ginsberg's room in Hamilton Hall to complain about the window-writing, he almost caught Kerouac in bed with Ginsberg.

English teachers should never have a Keats, Christopher Smart, Ginsberg or Kerouac alive in class, and Diana Trilling's essay 'The Other Night at Columbia' reminds us of the problem. Trilling and Van Doren were kindly and tolerant, but the nation's ethos was violent and fractured. In the Depression of the 1930s and during the war Americans had drawn together, but the war years had changed the social structure. In 1939 the United States had only four million taxpayers; in 1945 no less than 45 million were filing taxable returns (in a population of 140 million) as many labouring people had risen into the middle class. Suddenly these people lost their sense of cohesiveness and purpose which even the shortages, dislocations and sacrifices of war had given. In the late 1940s vicious strikes began. Life became a nervous quest for status and security, whatever the cost, in a lonely crowd. Truman's Fair Deal seemed bumbling and unfair. One heard the pun, 'To err is Truman.' And, after forty-four months of anxieties of war, President Truman had released an untested uranium bomb (not even the implosion-type plutonium bomb tested at Alamogordo) experimentally on Japan and seemed to have little sense of what he had done. *The New York Times* of 11 August 1945 had found Truman's remarks on the bomb weird, incredible, disturbing, as if the President were stunned because 'the gruesome fantasies of the "comic" strips were actually coming true'.

Then, in a speech that *The New York Times* printed in full, Stalin on the eve of Russian elections in February 1946 declared the cause of the war had been 'monopoly capitalism' and that the USSR was encircled by enemies. A month later Churchill, at Fulton, Missouri, made his memorable comment that 'from Stettin in the Baltic to Trieste in the Adriatic, an iron curtain has descended across the continent' and that Warsaw, Berlin, Prague, Vienna, Budapest, Belgrade, Bucharest, and

Sofia were enslaved. 'Last time I saw it all coming', said Churchill as he compared the Soviet threat with Hitler, 'and cried aloud to my own fellow countrymen and the world, but no one paid any attention.' Inside America, as the poet Archibald Macleish wrote in *Atlantic Monthly* in 1949, the Russian conquest of the American people had begun. Macleish meant Americans were now guided by Russians in offering a bitter opposing policy, a mirror-image, to nearly anything the Soviet Union did or proposed. *No. self-image*

It was in this atmosphere that General Eisenberg, or Ike, became president of Columbia University and then of the nation. An ironical fate sent him to a place where Ginsberg and Kerouac had been. When told there were exceptional physicists and chemists on his staff, Ike asked if they were also 'exceptional Americans'. Don't send him a long note, people at Columbia said, or his lips will get tired. 'Dear Eisenhower', Kerouac wrote with a friend, 'We love you—You're the great big white father. We'd like to fuck you.' Ferlinghetti wanted to impeach him (and wrote a poem on the subject), but Ginsberg and Kerouac wrote dream-sketches with Eisenhower as the hero—and Kerouac explains that one *must* love Eisenhower if one is a child. However, if Ike's scorn for technocrats and love of America were appealing, his ineffectuality was more important. He took office as President of the US in 1953 during Senator McCarthy's witch-hunting of supposed Communists. When McCarthy attacked a teacher at Columbia University, Ike did nothing and indeed kept silent when McCarthy tried to defame Eisenhower's own friend and former companion-at-arms General Zwicker. US Army officers might have been dangerously demoralised, but Ike stated that he would 'remain aloof' since he would not compromise the nation's executive power. But what was that power, then, if it let a McCarthy with the instincts of a Hitler do what he wished to people? McCarthy was supported by Len Hall, chairman of the Republican party, and by senators such as Dirksen, Jenner, Knowland and Bridges. And the great white father, formerly president of Columbia and then of the nation, did nothing and said nothing to check McCarthyism.

Eisenhower became a profound symbol for the Beat writers. A good and capable man, the invader of Europe, he presided over a smugly opportunistic, spiritually weak America which had lost its way and become mechanical and inhuman.

'Howl' was at once a roar of protest against Eisenhower's America and a deeply moving, loving poem, in tears and beyond tears and directed against an ethos that kills or outlaws the spirit. It was meant to be recited. Ginsberg, in his performances, said its lines with gusto, gesticulating, screaming, begging, urging, and at least once after taking off his clothes:

I saw the best minds of my generation destroyed by madness, starving
      hysterical naked,
dragging themselves through the negro streets at dawn looking for an
      angry fix,
angelheaded hipsters burning for the ancient heavenly connection to
      the starry dynamo in the machinery of night,
who poverty and tatters and hollow-eyed and high sat up smoking
      in the supernatural darkness of cold-water flats floating
      across the tops of cities contemplating jazz,
who bared their brains to Heaven under the El and saw Mohammedan
      angels staggering on tenement roofs illuminated,
who passed through universities with radiant cool eyes hallucinating
      Arkansas and Blake-light tragedy among the scholars of war,
who were expelled from the academies for crazy & publishing
      obscene odes on the windows of the skull,
who cowered in unshaven rooms in underwear, burning their money in
      wastebaskets and listening to the Terror through the wall,
who got busted in their pubic beards returning through Laredo with a
      belt of marijuana for New York,
who ate fire in paint hotels or drank turpentine in Paradise Alley, death,
      or purgatoried their torsos night after night. . . .

To Ginsberg's audiences, 'Howl' affirmed the spiritual life and integrity of each individual. His hipsters in their dreams and drugs, 'alcohol and cocks and endless balls', who let themselves be 'fucked in the ass by saintly motorcyclists' and had a 'vision of ultimate cunt' and who 'cut their wrists three times success-

ively unsuccessfully' or 'were burned alive in their innocent
flannel suits on Madison Avenue', or who ended in asylums—
as his friend Carl Solomon did—were images of the soul in
reaction to Hiroshima and the Cold War and the materialism
of a modern, technological society:

> Moloch! Solitude! Filth! Ugliness! Ashcans and unobtainable
> dollars! Children screaming under the stairways! Boys
> sobbing in armies! Old men weeping in the parks!
> Moloch! Moloch! Nightmare of Moloch! Moloch the loveless!
> Mental Moloch! Moloch the heavy judger of men! . . .
> Moloch whose love is endless oil and stone! Moloch whose soul is
> electricity and banks! Moloch whose poverty is the specter
> of genius! Moloch whose fate is a cloud of sexless hydrogen!
> Moloch whose name is the Mind! . . .
> Moloch! Moloch! Robot apartments!

If Moloch possesses the 'mind' and science turns nearly every
creed or illumination into 'bullshit', then possibly the beleagu-
ered soul may thrive among the locked-up and crazed—or
with Carl Solomon, the Jewish reader of Dostoevsky whom
Ginsberg met in the Columbia Psychiatric Institute. Ginsberg
was waiting to be assigned a bed when he heard Solomon
mention 'repentant mystics' and told him, 'I'm Myshkin' (a
reference to Dostoevsky's holy idiot) to which Solomon replied
'I'm Kirilov' (the nihilist in *The Possessed*).

> Carl Solomon! I'm with you in Rockland
> where you're madder than I am
> I'm with you in Rockland
> where you must feel very strange
> I'm with you in Rockland
> where you imitate the shade of my mother
> I'm with you in Rockland
> where you've murdered your twelve secretaries
> I'm with you in Rockland
> where you laugh at this invisible humor

I'm with you in Rockland
> where we are great writers on the same dreadful typewriter . . .

I'm with you in Rockland
> where fifty more shocks will never return your soul to its
> body again from its pilgrimage to a cross in the void . . .

I'm with you in Rockland
> in my dreams you walk dripping from a sea-journey on the
> highway across America in tears to the door of my cottage
> in the Western night

The making of a new literature

Ginsberg and Kerouac saw themselves not as political agitators, but as writers devoted to art, to technique. Kerouac spent months with Stendhal's *The Red and the Black* and Dostoevsky's *Brothers Karamazov*, studying methods scene by scene. When reading Hart Crane's *The Bridge*, he and Ginsberg walked to Brooklyn Bridge to compare its engineering with Crane's art. They discussed individual lines from Shakespeare, such as 'This is the Forest of Arden': where should the emphasis fall, what did it mean in dramatic context? With the wealthy, drug-taking William Burroughs they also explored the self. They had 'Dostoevskian confrontations' in which they criticized their feeling and its expression. Kerouac, who was bi-sexual, lived in Manhattan flats shared by six or fifteen other people, went to bed with two or three others at the same time. Though edgy about 'love', a commitment, and sometimes annoyed by Ginsberg's advances, he believed that bodies were to be used freely.

Burroughs had friends among conmen and gangsters, who stored guns or stolen goods in Kerouac's flat, but he knew all sides of New York. Kerouac accepted Bill Burroughs as part of a Balzacian education in the city. Drugs and alcohol were to be used not just for kicks but to discover new weird states of consciousness, and indulgence was to be paid for by a steady battering at one's typewriter, whatever one's head felt like. Kerouac typed so fast his machine sounded like static on the radio, a blur of sound resulting in heaps of words which came too quickly for sheets of paper; he began to write on scrolls of teletype paper. His subject was America and he compared himself to Thomas Wolfe of *Look Homeward, Angel* and learned from Wolfe's sensuous gigantism. His subject was importantly America *then*, with its House Un-American Activities Committee witch-hunts, regimentation of the average person, censorship of artists and film-makers, and Cold War (soon to be a hot war in Korea and Vietnam). 'The Cold War is the imposition of a vast mental barrier on everybody', Ginsberg later told the *Paris Review*. 'A hardening, a shutting off to the perception of desire and tenderness which everybody *knows*', and this makes for 'a self-consciousness which is the substitute for communication with the outside' and a 'fear of total feeling, really, total being.'

Ginsberg and Kerouac saw the worst obscenity as 'God is dead', and forgave friends for all but the fault of not being 'serious'. They themselves wasted time on alcohol and drugs, and lacked sleep and quiet routines, but two benefits accrued from their behaviour. Unlike many contemporary writers, including Lowell, Mailer, and Bellow, the Beats functioned as a group; Ginsberg and Kerouac prolonged their undergraduate days and benefited from mutual encouragement, intelligent talk and debate. Since they were mild and receptive in manner—at least before fame made Kerouac uncharacteristically boastful some nights, though even then he alienated few of his friends—they added other writers to their informal group besides Burroughs. Out at Berkeley, Ginsberg attached himself to a circle of San Francisco poets. He met Lawrence Ferlinghetti, a Sorbonne-educated seaman and poet who ran City Lights Bookstore and had a good sense of French and American literature. Ginsberg also renewed his friendship with Philip Lamantia, a poet born in San Francisco, though he had moved to New York, where he helped to edit the surrealist magazine *View*. Lamantia brought Caribbean mambo, Afro-Cuban rhythms and the importance of jazz fully into the reckonings of Beat writers, who imitated jazz in verse rhythms and in moods and patterns of their prose. Ginsberg met the poets Robert Duncan, Chris MacLaine, Gerd Stern, and Leonard Hall the Tibetan Buddhist scholar, but more important to him was a run-in in New York with a young, cherubic, prankish Italian-American and ex-criminal, Gregory Corso, who had sheaves of poems. Corso, at that time, was 21. (He had been an inept robber, it seems, too pleased with his plan to chat with his gang by walkie-talkie, and had spent three years on a robbery charge in Clinton Prison—a blessing, as it gave him time to write.)

First, then, their easy camaraderie helped Beats to know their nation. Second, it helped them to rid themselves of untested beliefs of that nation's culture. They tried to get *outside* America while living and observing *in it*, and studied the loving, detached Walt Whitman, Thoreau of Walden Pond, and Henry Miller alive at Big Sur. Nelson Algren, who was to telegraph his praise of *On the Road* to Kerouac, had shown in his own novels and stories an implicit patriotism with a severe criticism of city life and he had gone *outside* Chicago by diving into its drug-pushing lower depths (depicted in his novel, *The Man with the Golden Arm*). When I published my own Algren essay in Chicago's *New City* in 1964, the novelist J. T. Farrell was furious: the article, he wrote, 'seemed to me good until I thought about it. It is not criticism but a personal expression . . . about Nelson Algren', and Algren furthermore was only a novelist with a 'pretty good talent for blasting' (*New City*, 1 March 1964). But it was blasting in combination with his love for Chicago that made Algren palatable to the Beats, who valued writing that was clearly 'personal expression' and who felt that all they wrote had to come from what they had lived through. Their works are autobiographical because the only trusted viewpoint in Beat writing is an 'I'. No other voice can be honest enough to report the truth. Kerouac's heroes are not simply like Kerouac but, deeply, *are* Kerouac, as Sal Paradise is in *On the Road*. The voice speaking in Ginsberg's poems examines Ginsberg: he adopts no role, shelters behind no substitute and examines himself directly or indirectly in every poem he writes. So too the language in Beat works includes four-letter words since the authors used these words in talk. They used images which had impressed themselves on their minds, and did not try to seek for artificial pictures.

All is to begin with the self and yet, as in Whitman and Emerson, the self is a point of religious raying-out. For the Beats each person is born to wonder, dream, guess and hope, to relate to the cosmos through truths of ancestors; and Zen Buddhism, if a rich way, offers only one of the multiple interlacing truths of the spirit. Christian, Jewish, Hindu, Muslim and Zen ideas confirm each other with interchangeable symbols, so that Ginsberg, the Jew, finds the cross valid. But the cross is a beckoning image. Beyond the cornices of New York buildings, as Ginsberg and Kerouac felt in Times Square when neon advertising signs suffused the night sky with red, there was a holy architecture out in space asking them for a 'panoramic awareness'—but *that* implied looking at America itself. Though Beat writing is usually religious and mystical it is freed from any religious or mystical certainty in doctrine. It is Transcendental exactly in the New England sense of Emerson and Thoreau, since illuminations are to come from looking at the here and now, in this case, at the streets and geography of America. Fortunately in the 1950s, as a San Francisco renaissance in jazz and poetry overtook Greenwich Village in New York, Ginsberg and Kerouac had been having America interpreted for them by a young man who was 'on the road' and one of the best drivers alive—Neal Cassady.

Neal Cassady and the West

Young men bummed across America in the late 1940s and 1950s, as my brother Driz and I did. We never met Neal Cassady, though we wish we had, but we met young thugs who talked about America's beauty out in the desert or at Denver near the Rockies. To be on the road as we were in a 1925 Dodge car, or riding in boxcars, was to see and hear about that beauty. Even old jailbirds on railway-repair gangs could wonder aloud over America's landscape, and Neal Cassady had a good feeling for landscape. Raised by a drunken father in Denver, Cassady had been in and out of reform school; starting at age 14 he had stolen some 500 cars, and had earned a reputation as Denver's greatest 'cocksman'. When Kerouac met him in the 1940s Cassady had been reading

Schopenhauer, Nietzsche, Dumas and Proust to impress girls—but he wanted to write. He seemed as handsome as a movie cowboy, a Gene Autry, with a slim build and rugged but well-cut features. He talked to seduce and his comments on writing were good, as when he told Kerouac that one should write as if one were the first person on earth and was 'humbly and sincerely' putting down what one felt and saw, with sorrows and desires and 'passing thoughts'.

He was cool, easy, and generous, until he became restless; he let his wife Carolyn sleep with Kerouac for a time in a *ménage-à-trois*. And he was sublime behind a wheel. Swerving round a truck at 110 mph and turning his head, smiling and exulting, Cassady as Dean Moriarty becomes in *On the Road* more than an archetypal American: he is a saint of freedom who values experience, movement, and the beauty of loose, easy readiness. He is on a quest back and forth across America, in which questing itself is the goal. Even in real life this man's actions seemed symbolic: as Cassady risked all in the flick of a finger on the steering wheel, so in the instant of quick spontaneous writing the Beat poet throws his life into a phrase. And, since Kerouac and Ginsberg kept drifting back to bohemian intellectual New York, Cassady blew through that 'dragged-out end of the Columbia scene like a fresh wind from the West' (Joyce Johnson: *Minor Characters*.) American academies were choked by intellect and science. Poetry and novel-writing were in the hands of academically trained writers obsessed by taste, irony, innuendo, attenuated feeling and *New Yorker*-magazine niceties of style, so stifled they could not see how lifeless their work was. (The only intellectual to be trusted, the Beats felt, was one who valued feeling over reason.) Cassady was saved by instinct, boyish grace, impulse—moving and free like a latterday Huck Finn. Kerouac saw himself and Ginsberg and Cassady as a creative triangle, with Cassady perhaps as its apex—its guide, at least, from the West. Rivers, plains, deserts—over 3,000 miles of westwardness had made the American experience; the American mind responds to geography; and so Cassady (and *On the Road*) symbolised a terrain and its sources of renewal for the spirit.

Ginsberg recalls him best in 'The Green Automobile', and Kerouac, after *On the Road*, portrays him convincingly as Cody Pomeray in *Big Sur*, showing us a mellow hero after Cassady had served some time in prison on a minor drugs charge. John Clellon Holmes, a New England novelist four years Kerouac's junior (their birthday March 12 was the same), in turn depicts Cassady as Hart Kennedy in the Beat novel *Go*, although Holmes found Cassady's outlook less stimulating than Kerouac's 'special view of the world'. But for all his excess of charm, Cassady lacked self-discipline to survive for long, as man or writer: in 1968 he died of exposure on the railway tracks. A year later Kerouac's self-indulgent love for drink killed him at forty-seven.

The female hipster and women's liberation

If Neal Cassady was the hero of the Beats, was there any place for a heroine? In attacking the Beat Generation in the late 1950s, *Time*, *Life* and other American journals chiefly had males in mind. As Fred McDarrah in *Saga* (August 1960) noticed, for *Time* magazine Jack Kerouac was a depraved spokesman for young *men*, or the 'latrine house laureate of Hobohemia'. Can women be hoboes even if bohemians? In a Negro magazine, America's typical 'beatnik' (an unpatriotic word taking its suffix from the Russian *Sputnik*) is a 'pseudo-intellectual' who smokes reefers and lives 'in protest of something or other'. Had groups of women, since the suffragettes, often been known to 'protest'? *Life* doubted that 'pad-sharing' females could be many, but still some women, even nice, educated ones, were dropping out, going to live in Greenwich Village. The magazine looked into this phenomenon, and, to McDarrah's surprise, it ran a photo-essay showing a 'beat chick dressed in black' in her pad. Nearby were 'naked light bulbs, a hot plate for warming [the] expresso coffee pot and bean cans, a coal stove for heating baby's milk' and 'drying [the] chick's leotards'. To complete this forlornly truthful view, *Life* showed 'a beat baby, who has gone to sleep on the floor after playing with beer cans'.

This particular photo-essay may have been faked, but women

unquestionably were sharing their lives with bohemians. Artists and would-be's from San Francisco, attracted to New York because the scene was livelier and survival easier, had invaded Greenwich Village. They included poets, painters, photographers, dancers and jazz musicians, living in the east Village near warehouses and factory lofts and Fourth Avenue bookshops. In her vivid memoir *Minor Characters*, Joyce Johnson—who was then Kerouac's young lover—recalls the women. Their men took no jobs, but felt it was all right for a wife or girlfriend to work for wages since women had no creative endeavours to be distracted from; and, says Joyce, 'women didn't mind, or, if they did, they never said – not until years later.'

Kerouac and Ginsberg had powerful, claiming mothers, despite the fact that Ginsberg's mother spent many years in an asylum; Kerouac's beloved 'Mémère' took precedence over each of the three women he married. Beat women could be muses, angels, whores, or typists of the Great Male Work, but the only way they rose to fame was usually by spectacular death, as when Burroughs accidentally shot his wife Joan in Mexico City. Ginsberg in 1954 recorded a 'dream letter' from Clellon Holmes with the words, 'The social organization which is most true of itself to the artist is the boy gang', to which Ginsberg added in his journal, 'not society's perfum'd marriage'. For a woman, a relationship with a Beat writer was likely to be disastrous.

Joyce in her black sweater, black skirt and black stockings and hair hanging down over her shoulders waited in her apartment for Jack Kerouac. After making love, he liked to sleep alone. He was 'brotherly', and she listened when Jack and his friends talked. Always the voices of men, only the men, would fall and rise as beer glasses collected, she recalls. Cassady's wife Carolyn, who slept with her two men, similarly had been very grateful when a man asked her opinion. Mostly, 'Beat' women were as useful as robots might be, as visible as nondescript furniture, obedient as collies. One night Jack took Joyce to a Bleeker Street poetry recital; in a coffee shop a neat, trim-bearded black man was reading an 'academic' poem, with a few hip touches. Later he introduced himself: he was LeRoi Jones. Proud of Hetty Cohen, his girlfriend, he did the nicest possible thing and instead of talking about metaphors LeRoi graciously said, 'This woman over here is Hetty. . . .' That was enough; Hetty and Joyce were noticed, and in public could expect little more.

Their impasse was that a woman's notion of her selfhood was fixed by what men thought, and Kerouac had not examined that sort of oppression. Yet the Beats encouraged a change in at least two ways. They greatly valued feeling and spontaneity or a full, easy voicing of the self, and opposed all notions of social rank and race and ideas of hierarchy, including the idea that God is somehow privileged or above us. If Presidents and generals were to be seen as ridiculous and Eisenhower was only to be 'fucked' (literally and perhaps joyfully), the *next* idol to topple might be the American Male. Beat writing did speak for equality and honesty, and Jack did not mislead Joyce, though he hardly treated her well; he stumblingly tried to be her 'friend' or 'brother'; he did not try to shut her up. She behaved in his company as a nice Jewish girl from upper Manhattan might be expected to do in marriage, but was wiser when she left him.

Disliking marriage (though sometimes re-marrying), Beat writers saw friendship as preferable—a way of relating without claims. They condemned all static relationships and felt that in a muddying, blinding world playing with war and nuclear bombs, social connections were suspect. The self, the soul of each person must be heard; the body tells us about ourselves; masturbation is truthful and pure, not obliging. One's sexual partner ought to be chosen casually. In denying notions of obligation, the Beat writer implies that women have as much to gain from a new truth-to-self as men do. The Beat discovers that we are truly tender and gentle, not beings of violence, which is caused by a social order (under capitalism or communism) which represses wonder and love and viciously exalts technology and material values. In emphasizing the holy nature of the body, the Beat is not especially 'male' and would liberate us all; and a poet such as Sally Stern found it natural to write in a mode similar to that of other Beats. But although the Beat message was potentially liberating, in reality, the female hipster was not liberated. Most of her views were not greatly different from those of a Bronxville High School girl—and the suburban debutante became a 'beat chick' often enough to face rather genteel poverty in the Village. Still, thirty years later, and after the insights of feminism, one feels that some Beat attitudes about the self anticipated the future.

Beat techniques and their influence on modern writing
The Beats were certainly to affect the literature of subsequent decades; just as they had themselves drawn inspiration from earlier writers, especially from mainstreams in British and American poetry. Whitman above all is a beloved spirit for the Beats, as Ginsberg's 'Supermarket in California' shows in content and form. Whitman's free-verse line, his generous egotism, moral sensuality, interest in colours, textures, surfaces, and sounds of New York all echo poignantly in the California poem. Emily Dickinson's spontaneity and delicacy set a mark for Corso. And the deceptively casual 'Autobiography' by Ferlinghetti—a poem for jazz accompaniment—is a fine, deft sketch of a man who is defined with the help of Twain, Melville, and Thoreau, as well of course as Pound, Yeats, Eliot, and others. Moreover, Ginsberg for one is attentive to the rhythms of English prophetic verse, so that, for example, the cadences of Christopher Smart's *Jubilate Agno*

Let Noah and his company approach the throne of Grace, and do
    homage to the Ark of their Salvation . . .

may be heard faintly in 'Howl'

angelheaded hipsters burning for the ancient heavenly connection to the
    starry dynamo in the machinery of night.

Ginsberg, indeed, says that he was influenced by Smart, Blake, and others, but that he wrote 'Howl' mainly to satisfy Kerouac's sense of sound.

Kerouac's sound is determined by bop. In jazz a player improvises from the musical metrics of the instant; a syncopated melodic beat carries the musical improvisations up from level to level—as in Louis Armstrong's jazz. But bop, exemplified by Charlie Parker, frees jazz from the monotony of boring melodies, and moves up from level to level on sheer improvisations alone. Bop avoids meaning and fosters movement, free creation, and spontaneity. 'I'm the Bop writer', says Kerouac's hero in *The Subterraneans*, and for Ray Smith-as-Kerouac in *The Dharma Bums* Charlie Parker is king and 'founder of the Bop generation'. As bop frees itself from theme and exists in improvisation, so *On the Road* departs from conventional 'theme' and exists as movement, a movement between six cities or a mad tour with Sal Paradise saying 'Yes, he's mad' or 'Yes, he's my brother' as he clings to Dean Moriarty (Cassady) in a swing from New York to New Orleans, Mexico City, Denver, San Francisco and back to Chicago and New York.

Ginsberg and other Beats also admired the spontaneity of bop improvising. Ginsberg battered out the first part of 'Howl' in a mad rush to give it the flow 'Kerouac would like the sound of'; he took peyote to write the 'Moloch' passage. He drugged himself on amphetamine, morphine and Dexadrine to write 'Kaddish'—a failure—and left off drugs in despair, to return to them later. But Beat writers were not always 'high' when they wrote, nor did they often compose whole works at one sitting. Good phrases such as 'hydrogen jukebox' do not usually come easily. Most of the good Beat poems seem to have been composed on the principle of John Keats and Wilfred Owen: the draft is written quickly, perhaps with the help of notes, and then very carefully revised. But the bop inspiration is usually there.

Ginsberg's best poems have a strong, compelling social urgency, as though the fate of American society (perhaps of the globe) depended on whether one American, at last, could tell the truth about himself. An effect of improvised phrasing combines with delicacy in cadence in Ginsberg's 'Under the World', a poem as religious as Donne's Divine Sonnets or Hopkin's so-called Terrible Sonnets. Religious, too, is 'The Lion for Real', Ginsberg's tribute to his teacher Lionel Trilling.

'Death to Van Gogh's Ear!' is an important poem in that it elucidates Ginsberg's views of the political and economic present and the cultural past, even if its technique is not as fine as that in 'Supermarket', 'Under the World', 'Mescaline', 'The Green Automobile' or his relatively early 'Paterson'.

Gregory Corso's tonal range is greater, although his discoveries in sound are less important than Ginsberg's. He is almost conventionally lyrical in 'Horses' and 'Marriage'—good poems to read aloud to those new to the Beats—and even in these there is a 'bop' quality of seemingly free improvisation. 'The Thin Thin Line'—typically Beat in exploring a personal experience (the simple, humdrum, and yet bafflingly strange act of falling asleep)—and in contrast the wittily grand 'Ode to Old England & its Language' together suggest Corso's suppleness and variety as a poet. 'Columbia U Poesy Reading—1975' amusingly shows what time has given the Beats: fame, respect, less hair (at least in Ginsberg's case), self-doubt, perhaps more humility in thinking of forebears such as 'Emily D', Shelley, Southey, Chatterton, Coleridge, and De Quincey, and a wry (but not very serious) sense of failure with renewed self-love and pluck. Success hurts Beats—and its results are best explored in Kerouac's deeply honest *Big Sur*. (Ginsberg is badly served by his own *Collected Poems*, since he has written too many works in which sentiment and self-indulgence replace passion; only a small number of his poems are excellent.) Gary Snyder is the best poet of the lesser Beats, fresh and deft in exploring moods of his recollecting of recent experience. Lamantia is an authentic Beat in regarding the lyric as a means of spiritual quest.

Subsequent writers were influenced by these precedents. Through their jazz friends and poets such as LeRoi Jones, the Beats in the 1950s were in the vanguard of anti-racist feeling, which helped to spark off Civil Rights movements a decade later. They quickly influenced song-writing, and journalism. Protest songs carry the Beat note often. The New Journalism of Tom Wolfe in *Electric Kool Aid Acid Test* or *Fear of Loathing in Las Vegas* has a 'Beat' spontaneity in effect. Pirsig's *Zen and the Art of Motorcycle Maintenance* owes much to Kerouac's locating of meaning in movement. Journalism and semi-auto-biographical works may respond much more quickly to influences than do the conservative genres of biography and history. But the Beat influence has helped us to question our reportage on, and accounting for, the human past. We no longer think it absolutely truthful to account for past lives or events in a wholly retrospective way, as though, in the past, the future were already known, fixed and settled, or as though impredictability, emotional experience, and the 'feeling' of anyone's living through a day ought not to concern any historian. It seems significant that journalism, which records history of the present, on occasion took a new form in reporting the Vietnam War: piece after piece on Vietnam brought home to Americans the moods and immediate sensations of patrols in combat, and often in a prose deeply indebted to Kerouac. The Beats have brought literature closer to the texture of life, and their influence has not ended.

Kerouac's unusual sensibility is only now becoming clear to us. We perceive, for example, how each of his heroes determines the syntax and tone of each novel. We feel the difference between the nervous lucidity of *On the Road*, the long meandering 'bop'-style sentences in *The Subterraneans* which are attuned to its hero Leo, the notes of wonder and quest in the manner of *Dharma Bums* with its splendid landscapes and dialogues, and the elegiac, graphic, troubled, and yet often lyric manner of *Big Sur*. At their best Kerouac and Ginsberg are as artful as any other writers of this century, and so we may feel that just as the Beat movement has affected our ways of reporting on human experience, it has refreshed art itself, while producing more than one new and exciting American classic.

Park Honan, 1986

POETRY

ALLEN GINSBERG

A SUPERMARKET IN CALIFORNIA

What thoughts I have of you tonight, Walt Whitman, for I walked down the sidestreets under the trees with a headache self-conscious looking at the full moon.

In my hungry fatigue, and shopping for images, I went into the neon fruit supermarket, dreaming of your enumerations!

What peaches and what penumbras! Whole families shopping at night! Aisles full of husbands! Wives in the avocados, babies in the tomatoes!—and you, Garcia Lorca, what were you doing down by the watermelons?

I saw you, Walt Whitman, childless, lonely old grubber, poking among the meats in the refrigerator and eyeing the grocery boys.

I heard you asking questions of each: Who killed the pork chops? What price bananas? Are you my Angel?

I wandered in and out of the brilliant stacks of cans following you, and followed in my imagination by the store detective.

We strode down the open corridors together in our solitary fancy tasting artichokes, possessing every frozen delicacy, and never passing the cashier.

Where are we going, Walt Whitman? The doors close in an hour. Which way does your beard point tonight?

(I touch your book and dream of our odyssey in the supermarket and feel absurd.)

Will we walk all night through solitary streets? The trees add shade to shade, lights out in the houses, we'll both be lonely.

Will we stroll dreaming of the lost America of love past blue automobiles in driveways, home to our silent cottage?

Ah, dear father, graybeard, lonely old courage-teacher, what America did you have when Charon quit poling his ferry

3

and you got out on a smoking bank and stood watching the
boat disappear on the black waters of Lethe?

Berkeley 1955

THE LION FOR REAL

'Soyez muette pour moi, Idole contemplative . . .'

I came home and found a lion in my living room
Rushed out on the fire-escape screaming Lion! Lion!
Two stenographers pulled their brunette hair and banged the
    window shut
I hurried home to Paterson and stayed two days.

Called up my old Reichian analyst
who'd kicked me out of therapy for smoking marijuana
'It's happened' I panted 'There's a Lion in my room'
'I'm afraid any discussion would have no value' he hung up.

I went to my old boyfriend we got drunk with his girlfriend
I kissed him and announced I had a lion with a mad gleam in
    my eye
We wound up fighting on the floor I bit his eyebrow & he
    kicked me out
I ended masturbating in his jeep parked in the street moaning
    'Lion.'

Found Joey my novelist friend and roared at him 'Lion!'
He looked at me interested and read me his spontaneous ignu
    high poetries
I listened for lions all I heard was Elephant Tiglon Hippogryph
    Unicorn Ants
But figured he really understood me when we made it in Ignaz
    Wisdom's bathroom.

But next day he sent me a leaf from his Smokey Mountain
  retreat
'I love you little Bo-Bo with your delicate golden lions
But there being no Self and No Bars therefore the Zoo of your
  dear Father hath no Lion
You said your mother was mad don't expect me to produce the
  Monster for your Bridegroom.'

Confused dazed and exalted bethought me of real lion starved
  in his stink in Harlem
Opened the door the room was filled with the bomb blast of
  his anger
He roaring hungrily at the plaster walls but nobody could hear
  him outside thru the window
My eye caught the edge of the red neighbor apartment building
  standing in deafening stillness

We gazed at each other his implacable yellow eye in the red
  halo of fur
Waxed rheumy on my own but he stopped roaring and bared
  a fang greeting.
I turned my back and cooked broccoli for supper on an iron
  gas stove
boilt water and took a hot bath in the old tub under the sink
  board.

He didn't eat me, tho I regretted him starving in my presence.
Next week he wasted away a sick rug full of bones wheaten
  hair falling out
enraged and reddening eye as he lay aching huge hairy head
  on his paws
by the egg-crate bookcase filled up with thin volumes of
  Plato, & Buddha.

Sat by his side every night averting my eyes from his hungry
  motheaten face
stopped eating myself he got weaker and roared at night while
  I had nightmares

5

Eaten by lion in bookstore on Cosmic Campus, a lion myself
      starved by Professor Kandisky, dying in a lion's
      flophouse circus,
I woke up mornings the lion still added dying on the
      floor—'Terrible Presence!' I cried 'Eat me or die!'

It got up that afternoon—walked to the door with its paw on
      the wall to steady its trembling body
Let out a soul rending creak from the bottomless roof of his
      mouth
thundering from my floor to heaven heavier than a volcano at
      night in Mexico
Pushed the door open and said in a gravelly voice 'Not this
      time Baby—but I will be back again.'

Lion that eats my mind now for a decade knowing only your
      hunger
Not the bliss of your satisfaction O roar of the Universe how
      am I chosen
In this life I have heard your promise I am ready to die I have
      served
Your starved and ancient Presence O Lord I wait in my room
      at your Mercy.

Paris 1958

DEATH TO VAN GOGH'S EAR!

Poet is Priest
Money has reckoned the soul of America
Congress broken thru to the precipice of Eternity
the President built a War machine which will vomit and rear
      up Russia out of Kansas
The American Century betrayed by a mad Senate which no
      longer sleeps with its wife
Franco has murdered Lorca the fairy son of Whitman
just as Mayakovsky committed suicide to avoid Russia

Hart Crane distinguished Platonist committed suicide to cave
in the wrong America
just as millions of tons of human wheat were burned in secret
caverns under the White House
while India starved and screamed and ate mad dogs full of rain
and mountains of eggs were reduced to white powder in the
halls of Congress
no godfearing man will walk there again because of the stink
of the rotten eggs of America
and the Indians of Chiapas continue to gnaw their vitaminless
tortillas
aborigines of Australia perhaps gibber in the eggless wilderness
and I rarely have an egg for breakfast tho my work requires
infinite eggs to come to birth in Eternity
eggs should be eaten or given to their mothers
and the grief of the countless chickens of America is expressed
in the screaming of her comedians over the radio
Detroit has built a million automobiles of rubber trees and
phantoms
but I walk, I walk, and the Orient walks with me, and all Africa
walks
and sooner or later North America will walk
for as we have driven the Chinese Angel from our door he will
drive us from the Golden Door of the future
we have not cherished pity on Tanganyika
Einstein alive was mocked for his heavenly politics
Bertrand Russell driven from New York for getting laid
and the immortal Chaplin has been driven from our shores
with the rose in his teeth
a secret conspiracy by the Catholic Church in the lavatories of
Congress has denied contraceptives to the unceasing
masses of India.
Nobody publishes a word that is not the cowardly robot ravings
of a depraved mentality
the day of the publication of the true literature of the American
body will be the day of Revolution
the revolution of the sexy lamb
the only bloodless revolution that gives away corn

poor Genet will illuminate the harvesters of Ohio
Marijuana is a benevolent narcotic but J. Edgar Hoover prefers
    his deathly scotch
And the heroin of Lao-Tze & the Sixth Patriarch is punished
    by the electric chair
but the poor sick junkies have nowhere to lay their heads
fiends in our government have invented a cold-turkey cure for
        addiction as obsolete as the Defense Early Warning
        Radar System.
I am the defense early warning radar system
I see nothing but bombs
I am not interested in preventing Asia from being Asia
and the governments of Russia and Asia will rise and fall but
        Asia and Russia will not fall
the government of America also will fall but how can America
    fall
I doubt if anyone will ever fall anymore except governments
fortunately all the governments will fall
the only ones which won't fall are the good ones
and the good ones don't yet exist
But they have to begin existing they exist in my poems
they exist in the death of the Russian and American
        governments
they exist in the death of Hart Crane & Mayakovsky
Now is the time for prophecy without death as a consequence
the universe will ultimately disappear
Hollywood will rot on the windmills of Eternity
Hollywood whose movies stick in the throat of God
Yes Hollywood will get what it deserves
Time
Seepage of nerve-gas over the radio
History will make this poem prophetic and its awful silliness a
        hideous spiritual music
I have the moan of doves and the feather of ecstasy
Man cannot long endure the hunger of the cannibal abstract
War is abstract
the world will be destroyed
but I will die only for poetry, that will save the world

8

Monument to Sacco & Vanzetti not yet financed to ennoble
    Boston
natives of Kenya tormented by idiot con-men from England
South Africa in the grip of the white fool
Vachel Lindsay Secretary of the Interior
Poe Secretary of Imagination
Pound Secty. Economics
and Kra belongs to Kra, and Pukti to Pukti
crossfertilization of Blok and Artaud
Van Gogh's Ear on the currency
no more propaganda for monsters
and poets should stay out of politics or become monsters
I have become monsterous with politics
the Russian poet undoubtedly monsterous in his secret
    notebook
Tibet should be left alone
These are obvious prophecies
America will be destroyed
Russian poets will struggle with Russia
Whitman warned against this 'fabled Damned of nations'
Where was Theodore Roosevelt when he sent out ultimatums
    from his castle in Camden
Where was the House of Representatives when Crane read
    aloud from his prophetic books
What was Wall Street scheming when Lindsay announced the
    doom of Money
Were they listening to my ravings in the locker rooms of
    Bickfords Employment Offices?
Did they bend their ears to the moans of my soul when I
    struggled with market research statistics in the Forum
    at Rome?
No they were fighting in fiery offices, on carpets of heartfailure,
    screaming and bargaining with Destiny
fighting the Skeleton with sabres, muskets, buck teeth, indiges-
    tion, bombs of larceny, whoredom, rockets, pederasty,
back to the wall to build up their wives and apartments, lawns,
    suburbs, fairydoms,

Puerto Ricans crowded for massacre on 114th St. for the sake
of an imitation Chinese-Moderne refrigerator
Elephants of mercy murdered for the sake of an Elizabethan
birdcage
millions of agitated fanatics in the bughouse for the sake of the
screaming soprano of industry
Money-chant of soapers—toothpaste apes in television
sets—deodorizers on hypnotic chairs—
petroleum mongers in Texas—jet plane streaks among the
clouds—
sky writers liars in the face of Divinity—fanged butchers of
hats and shoes, all Owners! Owners! Owners! with
obsession on property and vanishing Selfhood!
and their long editorials on the fence of the screaming negro
attacked by ants crawled out of the front page!
Machinery of a mass electrical dream! A war-creating Whore
of Babylon bellowing over Capitols and Academies!
Money! Money! Money! shrieking mad celestial money of
illusion! Money made of nothing, starvation, suicide!
Money of failure! Money of death!
Money against Eternity! and eternity's strong mills grind out
vast paper of Illusion!

Paris 1958

MESCALINE

Rotting Ginsberg, I stared in the mirror naked today
I noticed the old skull, I'm getting balder
my pate gleams in the kitchen light under thin hair
like the skull of some monk in old catacombs lighted by
a guard with flashlight
followed by a mob of tourists
so there is death
my kitten mews, and looks into the closet
Boito sings on the phonograph tonight his ancient song of
angels

Antinous bust in brown photograph still gazing down from my
    wall
a light burst from God's delicate hand sends down a wooden
    dove to the calm virgin
Beato Angelico's universe
the cat's gone mad and scraowls around the floor

What happens when the death gong hits rotting ginsberg on
    the head
what universe do I enter
death death death death death the cat's at rest
are we ever free of—rotting ginsberg
Then let it decay, thank God I know
thank who
thank who
Thank you, O lord, beyond my eye
the path must lead somewhere
the path
the path
thru the rotting shit dump, thru the Angelico orgies
Beep, emit a burst of babe and begone
perhaps that's the answer, wouldn't know till you had a kid
I dunno, never had a kid never will at the rate I'm going

Yes, I should be good, I should get married
find out what it's all about
but I can't stand these women all over me
smell of Naomi
erk, I'm stuck with this familiar rotting ginsberg
can't stand boys even anymore
can't stand
can't stand
and who wants to get fucked up the ass, really?
Immense seas passing over
the flow of time
and who wants to be famous and sign autographs like a movie
    star

I want to know
I want I want ridiculous *to know to know* WHAT rotting
      ginsberg
I want to know what happens after I rot
because I'm already rotting
my hair's falling out I've got a belly I'm sick of sex
my ass drags in the universe I know too much
and not enough
I want to know what happens after I die
well I'll find out soon enough
do I really need to know now?
is that any use at all use use use
death death death death death
god god god god god god god the Lone Ranger
the rhythm of the typewriter
What can I do to Heaven by pounding on Typewriter
I'm stuck change the record Gregory ah excellent he's doing
      just that
and I am too conscious of a million ears
at present creepy ears, making commerce
too many pictures in the newspapers
faded yellowed press clippings
I'm going away from the poem to be a dark contemplative

trash of the mind
trash of the world
man is half trash
all trash in the grave

What can Williams be thinking in Paterson, death so much on
      him
so soon so soon
Williams, what is death?
Do you face the great question now each moment
or do you forget at breakfast looking at your old ugly love in
      the face
are you prepared to be reborn
to give release to this world to enter a heaven

or give release, give release
and all be done—and see a lifetime—all eternity—gone over
into naught, a trick question proposed by the moon to the
      answerless earth
No Glory for man! No Glory for man! No glory for me! No me!

No point writing when the spirit doth not lead

NY, 1959

UNDER THE WORLD THERE'S A LOT OF ASS, A LOT OF CUNT

a lot of mouths and cocks,
under the world there's a lot of come, and a lot of saliva
      dripping into brooks,
There's a lot of Shit under the world, flowing beneath cities
      into rivers,
a lot of urine floating under the world,
a lot of snot in the world's industrial nostrils, sweat under the
      world's iron arm, blood
gushing out of the world's breast,
endless lakes of tears, seas of sick vomit rushing between
      hemispheres
floating toward Sargasso, old oily rags and brake fluids, human
      gasoline –
Under the world there's pain, fractured thighs, napalm burning
      in black hair, phosphorus eating elbows to bone
insecticides contaminating oceantide, plastic dolls floating
      across Atlantic,
Toy soldiers crowding the Pacific, B-52 bombers choking jungle
      air with vaportrails and brilliant flares
Robot drones careening over rice terraces dropping cluster
      grenades, plaster pellets spray into flesh, dragontooth
      mines & jellied fires fall on straw roofs and water buffalos,
perforating village huts with barbed shrapnel, trenchpits filled
      with fuel-gas-poison'd explosive powders –

Under the world there's broken skulls, crushed feet, cut
    eyeballs, severed fingers, slashed jaws,
Dysentery, homeless millions, tortured hearts, empty souls.
April 1973

THE GREEN AUTOMOBILE

If I had a Green Automobile
        I'd go find my old companion
        in his house on the Western ocean.
                Ha! Ha! Ha! Ha! Ha!

I'd honk my horn at his manly gate,
        inside his wife and three
        children sprawl naked
                on the living room floor.

He'd come running out
        to my car full of heroic beer
        and jump screaming at the wheel
                for he is the greater driver.

We'd pilgrimage to the highest mount
        of our earlier Rocky Mountain visions
        laughing in each other's arms,
                delight surpassing the highest Rockies,

and after old agony, drunk with new years,
        bounding toward the snowy horizon
        blasting the dashboard with original bop
                hot rod on the mountain

we'd batter up the cloudy highway
        where angels of anxiety
        careen through the trees
                and scream out of the engine.

We'd burn all night on the jackpine peak
        seen from Denver in the summer dark,
    forestlike unnatural radiance
        illuminating the mountaintop:

childhood youthtime age & eternity
    would open like sweet trees
    in the nights of another spring
        and dumbfound us with love,

for we can see together
    the beauty of souls
    hidden like diamonds
        in the clock of the world,

like Chinese magicians can
    confound the immortals
    with our intellectuality
        hidden in the mist,

in the Green Automobile
    which I have invented
    imagined and visioned
        on the roads of the world

more real than the engine
    on a track in the desert
    purer than Greyhound and
        swifter than physical jetplane.

Denver! Denver! we'll return
    roaring across the City & County Building lawn
    which catches the pure emerald flame
        streaming in the wake of our auto.

This time we'll buy up the city!
    I cashed a great check in my skull bank

> to found a miraculous college of the body
> up on the bus terminal roof.

But first we'll drive the stations of downtown,
poolhall flophouse jazzjoint jail
whorehouse down Folsom
to the darkest alleys of Larimer

paying respects to Denver's father
lost on the railroad tracks,
stupor of wine and silence
hallowing the slum of his decades,

salute him and his saintly suitcase
of dark muscatel, drink
and smash the sweet bottles
on Diesels in allegiance.

Then we go driving drunk on boulevards
where armies march and still parade
staggering under the invisible
banner of Reality—

hurtling through the street
in the auto of our fate
we share an archangelic cigarette
and tell each other's fortunes:

fames of supernatural illumination,
bleak rainy gaps of time,
great art learned in desolation
and we beat apart after six decades. . . .

and on an asphalt crossroad,
deal with each other in princely
gentleness once more, recalling
famous dead talks of other cities.

The windshield's full of tears,
      rain wets our naked breasts,
      we kneel together in the shade
            amid the traffic of night in paradise

and now renew the solitary vow
      we made each other take
      in Texas, once:
            I can't inscribe here. . . .

          . . . . . .

          . . . . . .

How many Saturday nights will be
      made drunken by this legend?
      How will young Denver come to mourn
            her forgotten sexual angel?

How many boys will strike the black piano
      in imitation of the excess of a native saint?
      Or girls fall wanton under his spectre in the high
            schools of melancholy night?

While all the time in Eternity
      in the wan light of this poem's radio
      we'll sit behind forgotten shades
            hearkening the lost jazz of all Saturdays.

Neal, we'll be real heroes now
      in a war between our cocks and time:
      let's be the angels of the world's desire
            and take the world to bed with us before
                 we die.

Sleeping alone, or with companion,
      girl or fairy sheep or dream,
      I'll fail of lacklove, you, satiety:
            all men fall, our fathers fell before,

but resurrecting that lost flesh
        is but a moment's work of mind:
        an ageless monument to love
             in the imagination:

memorial built out of our own bodies
        consumed by the invisible poem—
      We'll shudder in Denver and endure
           though blood and wrinkles blind our eyes.

So this Green Automobile:
        I give you in flight
        present, a present
           from my imagination.

We will go riding
        over the Rockies,
        we'll go on riding
           all night long until dawn,

then back to your railroad, the SP
        your house and your children
        and broken leg destiny
           you'll ride down the plains

in the morning: and back
        to my visions, my office
        and eastern apartment
           I'll return to New York.

NY 1953

PATERSON

What do I want in these rooms papered with visions of money?
How much can I make by cutting my hair? If I put new heels
      on my shoes,
bathe my body reeking of masturbation and sweat, layer upon

layer of excrement
dried in employment bureaus, magazine hallways, statistical
cubicles, factory stairways,
cloakrooms of the smiling gods of psychiatry;
if in antechambers I face the presumption of department store
supervisory employees,
old clerks in their asylums of fat, the slobs and dumbbells of
the ego with money and power
to hire and fire and make and break and fart and justify their
reality of wrath
and rumor of wrath to wrath-weary man,
what war I enter and for what a prize! the dead prick of
commonplace obsession,
harridan vision of electricity at night and daylight misery of
thumb-sucking rage.

I would rather go mad, gone down the dark road to Mexico,
heroin dripping in my veins,
eyes and ears full of marijuana,
eating the god Peyote on the floor of a mudhut on the border
or laying in a hotel room over the body of some suffering man
or woman;
rather jar my body down the road, crying by a diner in the
Western sun;
rather crawl on my naked belly over the tincans of Cincinnati;
rather drag a rotten railroad tie to a Golgotha in the Rockies;
rather, crowned with thorns in Galveston, nailed hand and foot
in Los Angeles, raised up to die in Denver,
pierced in the side in Chicago, perished and tombed in New
Orleans and resurrected in 1958 somewhere on Garret
Mountain,
come down roaring in a blaze of hot cars and garbage,
streetcorner Evangel in front of City Hall, surrounded by
statues of agonized lions,
with a mouthful of shit, and the hair rising on my scalp,
screaming and dancing in praise of Eternity annihilating the
sidewalk, annihilating reality,
screaming and dancing against the orchestra in the destructible

ballroom of the world,
blood streaming from my belly and shoulders
flooding the city with its hideous ecstasy, rolling over the
    pavements and highways
by the bayoux and forests and derricks leaving my flesh and
    my bones hanging on the trees.

New York, November 1949

GREGORY CORSO

HORSES

Joy to horses!
Horses by the sea are listening to me;
do you suppose they are listening to me,
breathing and heaving and neighing to me?
Horses of night are there;
horses of light and delight and nightmare,
they are there,
completely satisfied with the sea,
completely satisfied with me.

MARRIAGE

Should I get married? Should I be good?
Astound the girl next door with my velvet suit and faustus
                                                        hood?

Don't take her to movies but to cemeteries
tell all about werewolf bathtubs and forked clarinets
then desire her and kiss her and all the preliminaries
and she going just so far and I understanding why
not getting angry saying You must feel! It's beautiful to feel!
Instead take her in my arms against an old crooked tombstone
and woo her the entire night the constellations in the sky—

When she introduces me to her parents
back straightened, hair finally combed, strangled by a tie,
should I sit knees together on their 3rd degree sofa
and not ask Where's the bathroom?
How else to feel other than I am,
often thinking Flash Gordon soap—
O how terrible it must be for a young man
seated before a family and the family thinking
We never saw him before! He wants our Mary Lou!
After tea and homemade cookies they ask What do you do for
a living?

Should I tell them? Would they like me then?
Say All right get married, we're losing a daughter
but we're gaining a son—
And should I then ask Where's the bathroom?

O God, and the wedding! All her family and her friends
and only a handful of mine all scroungy and bearded
just wait to get at the drinks and food—
And the priest! he looking at me as if I masturbated
asking me Do you take this woman for your lawful wedded
wife?
And I trembling what to say say Pie Glue!
I kiss the bride all those corny men slapping me on the back
She's all yours, boy! Ha-ha-ha!
And in their eyes you could see some obscene honeymoon
going on—
Then all that absurd rice and clanky cans and shoes
Niagara Falls! Hordes of us! Husbands! Wives! Flowers!
Chocolates!
All streaming into cozy hotels
All going to do the same thing tonight
The indifferent clerk he knowing what was going to happen
The lobby zombies they knowing what
The whistling elevator man he knowing
The winking bellboy knowing
Everybody knowing! I'd be almost inclined not to do anything!
Stay up all night! Stare that hotel clerk in the eye!

Screaming: I deny honeymoon! I deny honeymoon!
running rampant into those almost climactic suites
yelling Radio belly! Cat shovel!
O I'd live in Niagara forever! in a dark cave beneath the Falls
I'd sit there the Mad Honeymooner
devising ways to break marriages, a scourge of bigamy
a saint of divorce—

But I should get married I should be good
How nice it'd be to come home to her
and sit by the fireplace and she in the kitchen
aproned young and lovely wanting my baby
and so happy about me she burns the roast beef
and comes crying to me and I get up from my big papa chair
saying Christmas teeth! Radiant brains! Apple deaf!
God what a husband I'd make! Yes, I should get married!
So much to do! like sneaking into Mr Jones' house late at night
and cover his golf clubs with 1920 Norwegian books
Like hanging a picture of Rimbaud on the lawnmower
like pasting Tannu Tuva postage stamps all over the picket
fence
like when Mrs Kindhead comes to collect for the Community
Chest
grab her and tell her There are unfavorable omens in the sky!
And when the mayor comes to get my vote tell him
When are you going to stop people killing whales!
And when the milkman comes leave him a note in the bottle
Penguin dust, bring me penguin dust, I want penguin dust—

Yet if I should get married and it's Connecticut and snow
and she gives birth to a child and I am sleepless, worn,
up for nights, head bowed against a quiet window, the past
behind me,
finding myself in the most common of situations a trembling
man
knowledged with responsibility not twig-smear nor Roman coin
soup—
O what would that be like!

Surely I'd give it for a nipple a rubber Tacitus
For a rattle a bag of broken Bach records
Tack Della Francesca all over its crib
Sew the Greek alphabet on its bib
And build for its playpen a roofless Parthenon

No, I doubt I'd be that kind of father
not rural not snow no quiet window
but hot smelly tight New York City
seven flights up, roaches and rats in the walls
a fat Reichian wife screeching over potatoes Get a job!
And five nose running brats in love with Batman
And the neighbors all toothless and dry haired
like those hag masses of the 18th century
all wanting to come in and watch TV
The landlord wants his rent
Grocery store Blue Cross Gas & Electric Knights of Columbus
Impossible to lie back and dream Telephone snow, ghost
parking—
No! I should not get married I should never get married!
But—imagine If I were married to a beautiful sophisticated
woman
tall and pale wearing an elegant black dress and long black
gloves
holding a cigarette holder in one hand and a highball in the
other
and we lived high up in a penthouse with a huge window
from which we could see all of New York and even farther on
clearer days
No, can't imagine myself married to that pleasant prison
dream—

O but what about love? I forget love
not that I am incapable of love
it's just that I see love as odd as wearing shoes—
I never wanted to marry a girl who was like my mother
And Ingrid Bergman was always impossible
And there's maybe a girl now but she's already married

And I don't like men and—
but there's got to be somebody!
Because what if I'm 60 years old and not married,
all alone in a furnished room with pee stains on my underwear
and everybody else is married! All the universe married but
me!

Ah, yet well I know that were a woman possible as I am
possible

then marriage would be possible—
Like SHE in her lonely alien gaud waiting her Egyptian lover
so I wait—bereft of 2,000 years and the bath of life.

THE THIN THIN LINE

How easy it is to go to sleep.
To be awake and then not awake.
Half-death, sawing the log Z,
Or sheep hurdle
—I sleep smarter these nights;
That is, I don't give in so easily.
I want to know what it is puts me out,
Click, out, just like that, Z,
Every night of my life.

You'd think I'd lose sleep
Lying awake like that
Waiting for the *click*.
Nay, I stayed up for two nights
Thus to make sure the third night
Would have me very tired. I was.
I lay on the bed, eyes opened,
Waiting the moment before Z,
That thin thin line
Between wake and sleep.

It began to happen.
I was falling asleep.
I was conscious of it.
I—but watching it like that
Kept me awake.
If I wanted to fall asleep
I had not to be conscious.
It was hard. It was very hard.
I was lying on the bed.
I was tired, awfully tired.
I knew I could easily fall asleep
If I didn't keep watch for it to happen.

I woke up
Ignorant of what put me to sleep.

ODE TO OLD ENGLAND & ITS LANGUAGE

To express what's seen, what's heard, imagined,
          dreamed,
to hear, to read, to write, to speak—curse, console,
          weep, laugh, O hybrid responsible irresponsible
champion of idea, lie, truth, platitudes, battered jargon,
                    giant & dwarf altongue—
Paragnosis, splacturion, Spirit of the Barns, EAGLMDS,
          O silver alphabet in joy full return
to every tribe fresh and raw, clothed in animal,
          scamping swamps and forests, bear-baiting,
          firth-skimping, death-brothering,
to Gaels hording across the August bar;
          the Damnonian dusky promontory haycocking,
          setting hammer,
breast-rattling sun-shrieked beakers & horners, Cantii,
          massed visage, Wotin, hark! The England stretches
          away.

Bygone service, settlement mighty and sure,
    Trinobantes herald toward Essex, Middlesex,
      directionward;
        Iceni to Norfolk, Suffolk;
Cassii to Herts, Bucks, Bedford, onward; Coritani beaconed;
    Brigantes angled, and lo, the Belgae
           set their tents for settlement's end—
    The memories of all the years of that beginning,
        the hunting, the hawking,
      weaponed men and free-necked men;
legs clothed in red and blue, bandaged crossways from
    ankle to knee,
      the horned hat, the fierce braids and whiskers,
               fur smell, rawflesh shields;
chiefs dreaming heaven a vast hunt and feast,
      fearing hell an endless 4th season;
      and ladies in tight bodices fasten their mantles
             with wrought butterflies.

Tew, Freya, Saeter, the coming of Eostre;
the Mawy Clod's wolf-head ransom lain in the barrows,
    cromlechs;
      the Witena-gemot gathered in tribune,
        dole of free grain;
      theowes from frocland and bocland; than and
      ceorl;
Cyning and Etheling; sing, old vate, sing,
      wheat, barley, oat, rye, breathe the pastoral
      advance,
        all blast brown red yellow orange,
      sheep, cattle, swine, hardy tiller, earthbearer,
    soilwomber, kings & knights whistle across your fields;
lulled by firelight in your wicker domicile
      dreamed you chainless gold on the wrists of men?
      Good old Albion,
        crib of liberty.

Stonemeet oaken Druids teaching and judging,
their rite-drenched fingers directed toward the sun, moon,
    fire, water;
    splendors of wrong medicine, the laughing snake,
human spirits in the mice-clouds which veil the owl's brain;
dominion dance of brown-thoughts, skull-drink to compass
    the eye;
        Uraeus, Uraeus, loom from the East, rise, climb, bend,
            manifest each human sacrifice; summon a new
                magic,
a noumenal rune; drop harmless toothwort on the salver—
        And sat Caesar, as all waiting Decembers know,
            with burning head before the banks of Stour;
Cassivelaunus gathering clan after clan, all enjoinment,
                Briton entire;
yet destiny holds more than the ephemeral alliance of
    seasons and men;
    the brave tears of so early a nation fell,
    and falling stained all weathers hencefrom Verulam
—the sue for peace a vulnerable Argos never knew.

        There be boars yet to spike; all's not grunting,
                wailing, woe;
look to Horsa at Aylesford, Danes belching mead in the yews;
        no echo of Ostorius facing Caradoc at Caer Caradoc,
but laughing Boadicea over osseous heaps of Rome;
        the palsied make path for William—
    Londinium rings; fall the Cheviots, the sacred oaks;
benevolent Agricola complete, all-eyed navigator,
                'tis an isle, Albion's an isle;
                hold it well,
fort the Firths of Forth and Clyde; wall Solway to the Tyne;
        friars outflock Mons Graupias;
                bury Galgacus deep;
Carausius *Comes littoris Saxonica;* fall the Orkneys;
                down Rome, down.

Hail Britannia Prima, Britannia Secunda, Flavia,
Maxima Caesariensis, Valentia, Vespasiana;
England full-named!
Eboracum to York, Camalodunum to Colchester, Thermae
to Bath,
Isca Colonia to Caerleon, Rhutuple to Richborough—
And the Venerable Bede bent in labor in God's
scriptorium,
ignoring the abbot and his visitor in resplendent
surcoat,
to record a Caedmonian hymn, England's first poem—
And King Alfred the Encourager building abbeys and
schools;
old Albion closes;
England opens, "Lo! we have listened to many a lay
Of the Spear-Danes' fame, their splendors
of old,
Their mighty princes and martial deeds—"

WRIT ON THE STEPS OF
PUERTO RICAN HARLEM

There's a truth limits man
A truth prevents his going any farther
The world is changing
The world *knows* it's changing
Heavy is the sorrow of the day
The old have the look of doom
The young mistake their fate in that look
This is truth
But it isn't *all* truth

Life has meaning
And I do not know the meaning
Even when I felt it were meaningless
I hoped and prayed and sought a meaning
It wasn't all frolic poesy

There were dues to pay
Summoning Death and God
I'd a wild dare to tackle Them
Death proved meaningless without Life
Yes the world is changing
But Death remains the same
It takes man away from Life
The only meaning he knows
And usually it is a sad business
This Death

I'd an innocence I'd a seriousness
I'd a humor save me from amateur philosophy
I am able to contradict my beliefs
I am able able
Because I want to know the meaning of everything
Yet sit I like a brokenness
Moaning: Oh what responsibility
I put on thee Gregory
Death and God
Hard hard it's hard

I learned life were no dream
I learned truth deceived
Man is not God
Life is a century
Death an instant

AMERICA POLITICA HISTORIA, IN SPONTANEITY

O this political air so heavy with the bells
and motors of a slow night, and no place to rest
but rain to walk—How it rings the Washington streets!
The umbrella'd congressmen; the rapping tires
of big black cars, the shoulders of lobbyists
caught under canopies and in doorways,

and it rains, it will not let up,
and meanwhile lame futurists weep into Spengler's
prophecy, will the world be over before the races blend color?
All color must be one or let the world be done—
There'll be a chance, we'll all be orange!
I don't want to be orange!
Nothing about God's color to complain;
and there is a beauty in yellow, the old Lama
in his robe the color of Cathay;
in black a strong & vital beauty,
Thelonious Monk in his robe of Norman charcoal—
And if Western Civilization comes to an end
(though I doubt it, for the prophet has not
executed his prophecy) surely the Eastern child
will sit by a window, and wonder
the old statues, the ornamented doors;
the decorated banquet of the West—
Inflamed by futurists I too weep in rain at night
at the midnight of Western Civilization;
Dante's step into Hell will never be forgotten by Hell;
the Gods' adoption of Homer will never be forgotten by the
       Gods;
the books of France are on God's bookshelf;
no civil war will take place on the fields of God;
and I don't doubt the egg of the East its glory—
Yet it rains and the motors go
and continued when I slept by that wall in Washington
which separated the motors in the death-parlor
where Joe McCarthy lay, lean and stilled,
ten blocks from the Capitol—
I could never understand Uncle Sam
his red & white striped pants his funny whiskers his starry hat:
how surreal Yankee Doodle Dandy, goof!
American history has a way of making you feel
George Washington is still around, that is
when I think of Washington I do not think of Death—
Of all Presidents I have been under
Hoover is the most unreal

and FDR is the most President-looking
and Truman the most Jewish-looking
and Eisenhower the miscast of Time into Space—
Hoover is another America, Mr. 1930
and what must he be thinking now?
FDR was my youth, and how strange to still see
his wife around.
Truman is still in Presidential time.
I saw Eisenhower helicopter over Athens
and he looked at the Acropolis like only Zeus could.
OF THE PEOPLE is fortunate and select.
FOR THE PEOPLE has never happened in America or
        elsewhere.
BY THE PEOPLE is the sadness of America.
I am not politic.
I am not patriotic.
I am nationalistic!
I boast well the beauty of America to all the people in Europe.
In me they do not see their vision of America.
O whenever I pass an American Embassy I don't know what
        to feel!
Sometimes I want to rush in and scream: 'I'm American!'
but instead go a few paces down to the American Bar
get drunk and cry: 'I'm no American!'
The men of politics I love are but youth's fantasy:
The fine profile of Washington on coins stamps & tobacco
        wraps
The handsomeness and death-in-the-snow of Hamilton.
The eyeglasses shoe-buckles kites & keys of Ben Franklin.
The sweet melancholy of Lincoln.
The way I see Christ, as something romantic & unreal, is the
        way I see them.
An American is unique among peoples.
He looks and acts like a boyman.
He never looks cruel in uniform.
He is rednecked portly rich and jolly.
White-haired serious Harvard, kind and wry.
A convention man a family man a rotary man & practical joker.

He is moonfaced cunning well-meaning & righteously mean.
He is Madison Avenue, handsome, in-the-know, and
       superstitious.
He is odd, happy, quicker than light, shameless, and heroic
Great yawn of youth!
The young don't seem *interested* in politics anymore.
Politics has lost its romance!
The 'bloody kitchen' has drowned!
And all that is left are those granite
façades of Pentagon, Justice, and Department—
Politicians do not know youth!
They depend on the old
and the old depend on them
and lo! this has given youth a chance
to think of heaven in their independence.
No need to give them liberty or freedom
where they're at—
When Stevenson in 1956 came to San Francisco
he campaigned in what he thought was an Italian section!
He spoke of Italy and Joe DiMaggio and spaghetti,
but all who were there, all for him,
were young beatniks! and when his car drove off
Ginsberg & I ran up to him and yelled:
'When are you going to free the poets from their attics!'
Great yawn of youth!
Mad beautiful oldyoung America has no candidate
the craziest wildest greatest country of them all!
and not one candidate—
Nixon arrives ever so temporal, self-made,
frontways sideways and backways,
could he be America's *against?* Detour to vehicle?
Mast to wind? Shore to sea? Death to life?
The last President?

COLUMBIA U POESY READING—1975

PROLOGUE

What a 16 years it's been
Since last sat I here
with the Trillings again seated
he older . . . sweetly sadder;
she broader . . . unmotherly still

with all my poetfriends
ex-wife & forever daughter
with all my hair
and broken nose
and teeth no longer there
and good ol Kerouacky . . . poofed into fat air
Eterne Spirit of the Age . . . a
Monumental loss . . . another angel
chased from the American door

And what the gains?
Al volleyed amongst Hindu gods
then traded them all for Buddha's no-god
A Guggenheim he got; an NBA award;
an elect of the Academy of Arts & Sciences:
and the New York Times paid him 400 dollars
for a poem he wrote about being mugged for 60 dollars
O blessed fortune! for his life
there is no thief

16 years ago we were put down
for being filthy beatnik sex commie dope fiends
Now—16 years later Allen's the respect of his elders
the love of his peers
and the adulation of millions of youth . . .
Peter has himself a girl so that he and Allen,
Hermes willing, might have a baby
He's also a farm and a tractor

and fields and fields of soybeans
Bill's ever Bill
even though he stopped drugging and smoking cigarettes
Me, I'm still considered an unwashed beatnik sex commie dope
      fiend
True, I don't bathe every day (deodorants kill
the natural redolence of the human form divine)
and sex, yes, I've made three fleshed angels in life;
and I'm as much a Communist as I am a Capitalist
i.e., I'm incapable of being either of 'em;
as for Dopey-poo, it be a poet's porogative

Dear Audience,
we early heads of present style & consciousness
(with Kerouac in spirit)
are the Daddies of the Age
16 years ago, born of ourselves,
ours was a history with a future
And from our Petroniusian view of society
a subterranean poesy of the streets
enhanced by the divine butcher: humor,
did climb the towers of the Big Lie
and boot the ivory apple-cart of tyrannical values
into illusory oblivion
without spilling a drop of blood
  . . . blessed be Revolutionaries of the Spirit!

POEM

Summoned by the Muse
I expected the worst
Outside Her Sanctum Sanctorum
I paced up and down a pylon
of alabaster poets
known and unknown by name
and lauded and neglect of fame
I felt weak and afeared

and swore to myself:
"This is it! It's good-bye poetry for me!"
And the eyes of Southey
humbled me
into a nothingness
I braced myself
with self-assurances
muttering: 'Being a poet
limits one's full potential;
I can ride Pegasus anytime I feel;
though my output has been of late
seldom and chance,
it's the being makes the poem
not the poem the being:
and besides, I long ago announced myself poet
long before the poem—"
The great Thothian doors opened
I beheld Her and exclaimed: 'Ah, Miss God!'
She beckoned me sit upon a velvety gold cushion
I sat—and at Her swan-boned feet sat three:
Ganesha, Thoth, Hermes,
and over a pipe of Edgar Poe's skullen ash
they blew a fiery diamond of Balbeckian hash
"O charming poet-stud whom I adore
my Nunzio Corso Gregorio
I twirl churingas, I sing,
you inspire the inspirer
for behold I am the Muse
and music is my sacrament
—I ask you, would you ever deny me?"
"Never!" I swore . . .
From Ganesha's curled trunk to Thoth's ibis beak
to Hermes' Praxitelesean nose She flecked cocaine
from the Dawnman's mirrory brain—
"Would you favor me your ear?"
"Happily so O sweet sister of sestinas"
"It's Emily, Emily D . . .
I implore you regard her chemicry

she who tested a liquor never brewed;
and Percy Bysshe, your beloved Shelley
who of laudanum did partake
. . . but I fear I'll embarrass you
this question I would put to you . . ."
"O soul of Shakespeare, ask me, ask me anything . . ."
I could hear the silent laughter
of Her three messenger-boys
"I have no desire to upset you—"
"Ask; I shall answer"
"What thinkest thou the poppy?"
My silence seemed the lapse of a decade
The eyes of She and the three
were like death chills waved upon me
When I finally spoke I spoke a voice
old so old and far from the child I used to be
"Dear carefree girl of Homer, Madonna of Rimbaud;
morphia is poet-old,
an herbal emetic of oraclry,
an hallucinatory ichor divined by thee
as traditioned unto the bards of the Lake,
theirs and mine to use at liberty
but I am not free to be at such liberty;
the law has put its maw
into the poet's medicine cabinet
. . . I tell you, O sweet melancholy of Chatterton,
the forces of morality
and depresséd gangs of youth,
this God-sick age
and fields farmed by gangster farmers
prevents the poet ferret his mind
halts him his probe of the pain of life
. . . for consider, around that Lake
Coleridge and De Quincey were spared
the Eldorado Caddie connection men
and every other Puerto Rican mother's son
has his stash of laudanum
—for me there is no Xanadu"

"I ask you: Do you favor heroin more than you do me?"
The three each held a bloody needle
each needle a familiarity
"Was I with you when heroin was with you?"
A great reality overcame me
huge as death, indeed death—
The hash, an illusion, was in truth myrrh,
and the cocaine, illusion, was the white dust of Hermes'
       wings
Again Her awful tone:
        "Do you love drugs more than you love me?"
"I'm not ashamed!" I screamed
"You have butchered your spirit!" roared Ganesha
"Your pen is bloodied!" cawed the scribe Thoth
"You have failed to deliver the Message!" admonished Hermes
With tearful eyes I gazed into Her eyes and cried:
"I swear to you there is in me yet time
to run back through life and expiate
all that's been sadly done . . . sadly neglected . . ."

Seated on a cold park bench
I heard Her moan: "O Gregorio, Gregorio
you'll fail me, I know"

Walking away
a little old lady behind me
was singing: "True! True!"
"Not so!" rang the spirit, "Not so!"

LAWRENCE FERLINGHETTI

AUTOBIOGRAPHY

    I am leading a quiet life
    in Mike's Place every day
    watching the champs

of the Dante Billiard Parlor
and the French pinball addicts.
I am leading a quiet life
on lower East Broadway.
I am an American.
I was an American boy.
I read the American Boy Magazine
and became a boy scout
in the suburbs.
I thought I was Tom Sawyer
catching crayfish in the Bronx River
and imagining the Mississippi.
I had a baseball mit
and an American Flyer bike.
I delivered the Woman's Home Companion
at five in the afternoon
or the Herald Trib
at five in the morning.
I still can hear the paper thump
on lost porches.
I had an unhappy childhood.
I saw Lindberg land.
I looked homeward
and saw no angel.
I got caught stealing pencils
from the Five and Ten Cent Store
the same month I made Eagle Scout.
I chopped trees for the CCC
and sat on them.
I landed in Normandy
in a rowboat that turned over.
I have seen the educated armies
on the beach at Dover.
I have seen Egyptian pilots in purple clouds
shopkeepers rolling up their blinds
at midday
potato salad and dandelions
at anarchist picnics.

I am reading 'Lorna Doone'
and a life of John Most
terror of the industrialist
a bomb on his desk at all times.
I have seen the garbagemen parade
in the Columbus Day Parade
behind the glib
farting trumpeters.
I have not been out to the Cloisters
in a long time
nor to the Tuileries
but I still keep thinking
of going.
I have seen the garbagemen parade
when it was snowing.
I have eaten hotdogs in ballparks.
I have heard the Gettysburg Address
and the Ginsberg Address.
I like it here
and I won't go back
where I came from.
I too have ridden boxcars boxcars boxcars.
I have travelled among unknown men.
I have been in Asia
with Noah in the Ark.
I was in India
when Rome was built.
I have been in the Manger
with an Ass.
I have seen the Eternal Distributor
from a White Hill
in South San Francisco
and the Laughing Woman at Loona Park
outside the Fun House
in a great rainstorm
still laughing.
I have heard the sound of revelry
by night.

I have wandered lonely
as a crowd.
I am leading a quiet life
outside of Mike's Place every day
watching the world walk by
in its curious shoes.
I once started out
to walk around the world
but ended up in Brooklyn.
That Bridge was too much for me.
I have engaged in silence
exile and cunning.
I flew too near the sun
and my wax wings fell off.
I am looking for my Old Man
whom I never knew.
I am looking for the Lost Leader
with whom I flew.
Young men should be explorers.
Home is where one starts from.
But Mother never told me
there'd be scenes like this.
Womb-weary
I rest
I have travelled.
I have seen goof city.
I have seen the mass mess.
I have heard Kid Ory cry.
I have heard a trombone preach.
I have heard Debussy
strained thru a sheet.
I have slept in a hundred islands
where books were trees.
I have heard the birds
that sound like bells.
I have worn grey flannel trousers
and walked upon the beach of hell.
I have dwelt in a hundred cities

where trees were books.
What subways what taxis what cafes!
What women with blind breasts
limbs lost among skyscrapers!
I have seen the statues of heroes
at carrefours.
Danton weeping at a metro entrance
Columbus in Barcelona
pointing Westward up the Ramblas
toward the American Express
Lincoln in his stony chair
And a great Stone Face
in North Dakota.
I know that Columbus
did not invent America.
I have heard a hundred housebroken Ezra Pounds.
They should all be freed.
It is long since I was a herdsman.
I am leading a quiet life
in Mike's Place every day
reading the Classified columns.
I have read the Reader's Digest
from cover to cover
and noted the close identification
of the United States and the Promised Land
where every coin is marked
In God We Trust
but the dollar bills do not have it
being gods unto themselves.
I read the Want Ads daily
looking for a stone a leaf
an unfound door.
I hear America singing
in the Yellow Pages.
One could never tell
the soul has its rages.
I read the papers every day
and hear humanity amiss

in the sad plethora of print.
I see where Walden Pond has been drained
to make an amusement park.
I see they're making Melville
eat his whale.
I see another war is coming
but I won't be there to fight it.
I have read the writing
on the outhouse wall.
I helped Kilroy write it.
I marched up Fifth Avenue
blowing on a bugle in a tight platoon
but hurried back to the Casbah
looking for my dog.
I see a similarity
between dogs and me.
Dogs are the true observers
walking up and down the world
thru the Molloy country.
I have walked down alleys
too narrow for Chryslers.
I have seen a hundred horseless milkwagons
in a vacant lot in Astoria.
Ben Shahn never painted them
but they're there
askew in Astoria.
I have heard the junkman's obbligato.
I have ridden superhighways
and believed the billboard's promises
Crossed the Jersey Flats
and seen the Cities of the Plain
And wallowed in the wilds of Westchester
with its roving bands of natives
in stationwagons.
I have seen them.
I am the man.
I was there.
I suffered

somewhat.
I am an American.
I have a passport.
I did not suffer in public.
And I'm too young to die.
I am a selfmade man.
And I have plans for the future.
I am in line
for a top job.
I may be moving on
to Detroit.
I am only temporarily
a tie salesman.
I am a good Joe.
I am an open book
to my boss.
I am a complete mystery
to my closest friends.
I am leading a quiet life
in Mike's Place every day
contemplating my navel.
I am a part
of the body's long madness.
I have wandered in various nightwoods.
I have leaned in drunken doorways.
I have written wild stories
without punctuation.
I am the man.
I was there.
I suffered
somewhat.
I have sat in an uneasy chair.
I am a tear of the sun.
I am a hill
where poets run.
I invented the alphabet
after watching the flight of cranes
who made letters with their legs.

I am a lake upon a plain.
I am a word
in a tree.
I am a hill of poetry.
I am a raid
on the inarticulate.
I have dreamt
that all my teeth fell out
but my tongue lived
to tell the tale.
For I am a still
of poetry.
I am a bank of song.
I am a playerpiano
in an abandoned casino
on a seaside esplanade
in a dense fog
still playing.
I see a similarity
between the Laughing Woman
and myself.
I have heard the sound of summer
in the rain.
I have seen girls on boardwalks
have complicated sensations.
I understand their hesitations.
I am a gatherer of fruit.
I have seen how kisses
cause euphoria.
I have risked enchantment.
I have seen the Virgin
in an appletree at Chartres
And Saint Joan burn
at the Bella Union.
I have seen giraffes in junglejims
their necks like love
wound around the iron circumstances
of the world.

I have seen the Venus Aphrodite
armless in her drafty corridor.
I have heard a siren sing
at One Fifth Avenue.
I have seen the White Goddess dancing
in the Rue des Beaux Arts
on the Fourteenth of July
and the Beautiful Dame Without Mercy
picking her nose in Chumley's.
She did not speak English.
She had yellow hair
and a hoarse voice
and no bird sang.
I am leading a quiet life
in Mike's Place every day
watching the pocket pool players
making the minestrone scene
wolfing the macaronis
and I have read somewhere
the Meaning of Existence
yet have forgotten
just exactly where.
But I am the man
And I'll be there.
And I may cause the lips
of those who are asleep
to speak.
And I may make my notebooks
into sheaves of grass.
And I may write my own
eponymous epitaph
instructing the horsemen
to pass.

I HAVE NOT LAIN WITH BEAUTY
ALL MY LIFE . . .

I have not lain with beauty all my life
      telling over to myself
                its most rife charms

I have not lain with beauty all my life
              and lied with it as well
     telling over to myself
        how beauty never dies
    but lies apart
       among the aborigines
             of art
      and far above the battlefields
           of love

It is above all that
        oh yes
It sits upon the choicest of
       Church seats
up there where art directors meet
to choose the things for immortality

        And they have lain with beauty
    all their lives
       And they have fed on honeydew
and drunk the wines of Paradise
      so that they know exactly how
a thing of beauty is a joy
   forever and forever
       and how it never never
    quite can fade
      into a money-losing nothingness

Oh no I have not lain
      on Beauty Rests like this
  afraid to rise at night

for fear that I might somehow miss
some movement beauty might have made
Yet I have slept with beauty
in my own weird way
and I have made a hungry scene or two
with beauty in my bed
and so spilled out another poem or two
and so spilled out another poem or two
upon the Bosch-like world

THE POET'S EYE OBSCENELY SEEING . . .

The poet's eye obscenely seeing
sees the surface of the round world
with its drunk rooftops
and wooden oiseaux on clotheslines
and its clay males and females
with hot legs and rosebud breasts
in rollaway beds
and its trees full of mysteries
and its Sunday parks and speechless statues
and its America
with its ghost towns and empty Ellis Islands
and its surrealist landscape of
mindless prairies
supermarket suburbs
steamheated cemeteries
and protesting cathedrals
a kissproof world of plastic toiletseats tampax and taxis
drugged store cowboys and las vegas virgins
disowned indians and cinemad matrons
unroman senators and conscientious non-objectors
and all the other fatal shorn-up fragments
of the immigrant's dream come too true
and mislaid
among the sunbathers

UNDERWEAR

I didn't get much sleep last night
thinking about underwear
Have you ever stopped to consider
underwear in the abstract
When you really dig into it
some shocking problems are raised
Underwear is something
we all have to deal with
Everyone wears
some kind of underwear
Even Indians
wear underwear
Even Cubans
wear underwear
The Pope wears underwear I hope
The Governor of Louisiana
wears underwear
I saw him on TV
He must have had tight underwear
He squirmed a lot
Underwear can really get you in a bind
You have seen the underwear ads
for men and women
so alike but so different
Women's underwear holds things up
Men's underwear holds things down
Underwear is one thing
men and women have in common
Underwear is all we have between us
You have seen the three-color pictures
with crotches encircled
to show the areas of extra strength
and three-way stretch
promising full freedom of action
Don't be deceived

It's all based on the two-party system
which doesn't allow much freedom of choice
the way things are set up
America in its Underwear
struggles thru the night
Underwear controls everything in the end
Take foundation garments for instance
They are really fascist forms
of underground government
making people believe
something but the truth
telling you what you can or can't do
Did you ever try to get around a girdle
Perhaps Non-Violent Action
is the only answer
Did Gandhi wear a girdle?
Did Lady Macbeth wear a girdle?
Was that why Macbeth murdered sleep?
And that spot she was always rubbing—
Was it really in her underwear?
Modern anglosaxon ladies
must have huge guilt complexes
always washing and washing and washing
Out damned spot
Underwear with spots very suspicious
Underwear with bulges very shocking
Underwear on clothesline a great flag of freedom
Someone has escaped his Underwear
May be naked somewhere
Help!
But don't worry
Everybody's still hung up in it
There won't be no real revolution
And poetry still the underwear of the soul
And underwear still covering
a multitude of faults
in the geological sense—
strange sedimentary stones, inscrutable cracks!

If I were you I'd keep aside
an oversize pair of winter underwear
Do not go naked into that good night
And in the meantime
keep calm and warm and dry
No use stirring ourselves up prematurely
'over Nothing'
Move forward with dignity
hand in vest
Don't get emotional
And death shall have no dominion
There's plenty of time my darling
Are we not still young and easy
Don't shout

ADIEU À CHARLOT
(*Second Populist Manifesto*)

Sons of Whitman sons of Poe
sons of Lorca & Rimbaud
or their dark daughters
poets of another breath
poets of another vision
Who among you still speaks of revolution
Who among you still unscrews
the locks from the doors
in this revisionist decade?
'You are President of your own body, America'
Thus spoke Kush in Tepotzlan
youngblood wildhaired angel poet
one of a spawn of wild poets
in the image of Allen Ginsberg
wandering the wilds of America
'You Rimbauds of another breath'
sang Kush
and wandered off with his own particular paranoias

maddened like most poets
for one mad reason or another
in the unmade bed of the world
Sons of Whitman
in your 'public solitude'
bound by blood-duende
'President of your own body America'
Take it back from those who have maddened you
back from those who stole it
and steal it daily
The subjective must take back the world
from the objective gorillas & guerrillas of the world
We must rejoin somehow
the animals in the fields
in their steady-state meditation
'Your life is in your own hands still
Make it flower make it sing'
(so sang mad Kush in Tepotzlan)
'a constitutional congress of the body'
still to be convened to seize control
of the State
the subjective state
from those who have subverted it
The arab telephone of the avant-garde
has broken down
And I speak to you now
from another country
Do not turn away
in your public solitudes
you poets of other visions
of the separate lonesome visions
untamed uncornered visions
fierce recalcitrant visions
you Whitmans of another breath
which is not the too-cool breath of modern poetry
which is not the halitosis of industrial civilization
Listen now Listen again
to the song in the blood the dark duende a dark singing

between the tickings of civilization
between the lines of its headlines
in the silences between cars
driven like weapons
In two hundred years of freedom
we have invented
the permanent alienation of the subjective
almost every truly creative being
alienated & expatriated
in his own country
in Middle America or San Francisco
the death of the dream in your birth
o meltingpot America
I speak to you
from another country
another kind of blood-letting land
from Tepotzlan the poets' lan'
Land of the Lord of the Dawn
                              Quetzalcoatl
Land of the Plumed Serpent
I signal to you
as Artaud signaled
through the flames
I signal to you
over the heads of the land
the hard heads that stand like menhirs
above the land in every country
the short-haired hyenas
who still rule everything
I signal to you from Poets' Land
you poets of the alienated breath
to take back your land again
and the deep sea of the subjective
Have you heard the sound of the ocean lately
the sound by which daily
the stars still are driven
the sound by which nightly
the stars retake their sky

The sea thunders still to remind you
of the thunder in the blood
to remind you of your selves
Think now of your self
as of a distant ship
Think now of your beloved
of the eyes of your beloved
whoever is most beloved
he who held you hard in the dark
or she who washed her hair by the waterfall
whoever makes the heart pound
the blood pound
Listen says the river
Listen says the sea Within you
you with your private visions
of another reality a separate reality
Listen and study the charts of time
Read the sanskrit of ants in the sand
You Whitmans of another breath
there is no one else to tell
how the alienated generations
have lived out their expatriate visions
here and everywhere
The old generations have lived them out
Lived out the bohemian myth in Greenwich Villages
Lived out the Hemingway myth
in *The Sun Also Rises*
at the Dôme in Paris
or with the bulls at Pamplona
Lived out the Henry Miller myth
in the *Tropics* of Paris
and the great Greek dream
of *The Colossus of Maroussi*
and the tropic dream of Gauguin
Lived out the D. H. Lawrence myth
in *The Plumed Serpent*
in Mexico Lake Chapala
And the Malcolm Lowry myth

Under the Volcano at Cuernavaca
And then the saga of *On the Road*
and the Bob Dylan myth Blowing in the Wind
How many roads must a man walk down
How many Neal Cassadys on lost railroad tracks
How many replicas of Woody Guthrie with cracked guitars
How many photocopies of longhaired Joan
How many Ginsberg facsimiles and carbon-copy Keseys
still wandering the streets of America
in old tennis shoes and backpacks
or driving beat-up school buses
with destination-signs reading 'Further'
How many Buddhist Catholics how many cantors
chanting the Great Paramita Sutra
on the Lower East Side
How many Whole Earth Catalogs
lost in out-houses on New Mexico communes
How many Punk Rockers waving swastikas
Franco is dead but so is Picasso
Chaplin is dead but I'd wear his bowler
having outlived all our myths but his
the myth of the pure subjective
the collective subjective
the Little Man in each of us
waiting with Charlot or Pozzo
On every corner I see them
hidden inside their tight clean clothes
Their hats are not derbys they have no canes
but we know them
we have always
waited with them
They turn and hitch their pants
and walk away from us
down the darkening road
in the great American night

> *Tepotzlan '75—San Francisco '78*

GARY SNYDER

MID-AUGUST AT SOURDOUGH
MOUNTAIN LOOKOUT

Down valley a smoke haze
Three days heat, after five days rain
Pitch glows on the fir-cones
Across rocks and meadows
Swarms of new flies.

I cannot remember things I once read
A few friends, but they are in cities.
Drinking cold snow-water from a tin cup
Looking down for miles
Through high still air.

T-2 TANKER BLUES

Mind swarming with pictures, cheap magazines, drunk brawls,
    low books and days at sea; hatred of machinery and
    money & whoring my hands and back to move this
    military oil—
I sit on the boat-deck finally alone: borrowing the oiler's dirty
    cot, I see the Moon, white wake, black water & a few
    bright stars.
All day I read DeSade—I loathe that man—wonder on his
    challenge, seek sodomy & murder in my heart—& dig
    the universe as playful, cool, and infinitely blank—
DeSade and Reason and the Christian Love.
Inhuman ocean, black horizon, light blue moon-filled sky, the
    moon, a perfect wisdom pearl—old symbols, waves,
    reflections of the moon—those names of goddesses, the
    rabbit on its face, the myths, the tides,
Inhuman Altair—that 'inhuman' talk; the eye that sees all space

is socketed in this one human skull. Transformed. The
source of the sun's heat is the mind,
I will not cry Inhuman & think that makes us small and nature
great, we are, enough, and as we are—
Invisible seabirds track us, saviours come and save us.

Recall a cloud of little minnows about our anchored ship in the
green lagoon of Midway. Corpse of a frigate-bird on the
beach, a turtle-shell a foot across flesh clinging still—
And out through narrow reefs to sea again, a month to go to
Persia. All the big wood Buddhas in Japan could bob
these waves, unnoticed by a bird—
Yesterday was the taste of seawater as I swam; now crack my
joints, all that I see & miss & never lose floods in—
Damn me a fool last night in port drunk on the floor & damn
this cheap trash we read. Hawaiian workers shared us
beer in the long wood dredge-men's steel-men's girl-
less night drunk and gambling hall, called us strange
seamen *blala* and clasped our arms & sang real Hawaiian
songs,
Bearded and brown and all the blood of Pacific in them
laughing, tattered shirts and tin hats, three-o-five an
hour;
Damn me not I make a better fool. And there is nothing vaster,
more beautiful, remote, unthinking (eternal rose-red
sunrise on the surf—great rectitude of rocks) than man,
inhuman man,
At whom I look for a thousand light years from a seat near
Scorpius, amazed and touched by his concern and pity
for my plight, a simple star,
Then trading shapes again. My wife is gone, my girl is gone,
my books are loaned, my clothes are worn, I gave away
a car; and all that happened years ago. Mind & matter,
love & space are frail as foam on beer. Wallowing on
and on,
Fire spins the driveshaft of this ship, full of smooth oil &
noise—blood of the palms d'antan—sweet oil of the
gritty earth—embraced in welded plates of perfect steel.

CARTAGENA

Rain and thunder beat down and flooded the streets—
We danced with Indian girls in a bar,
     water half-way to our knees,
The youngest one slipped down her dress and danced
      bare to the waist.
The big negro deckhand made out with his girl on his lap
      in a chair her dress over her eyes
Coca-cola and rum, and rainwater all over the floor.
In the glittering light I got drunk and reeled through
     the rooms,
And cried, 'Cartagena! swamp of unholy loves!'
And wept for the Indian whores who were younger than me,
     and I was eighteen,
And splashed after the crew down the streets wearing
     sandals bought at a stall
And got back to the ship, dawn came,
     we were far out at sea.

Colombia 1948—Arabia 1958

RIPRAP

Lay down these words
Before your mind like rocks.
     placed solid, by hands
In choice of place, set
Before the body of the mind
     in space and time:
Solidity of bark, leaf, or wall
     riprap of things:
Cobble of milky way,
     straying planets,
These poems, people,
     lost ponies with

Dragging saddles—
   and rocky sure-foot trails.
The worlds like an endless
   four-dimensional
Game of *Go*.
   ants and pebbles
In the thin loam, each rock a word
   a creek-washed stone
Granite: ingrained
   with torment of fire and weight
Crystal and sediment linked hot
   all change, in thoughts,
As well as things.

PHILIP LAMANTIA

FUD AT FOSTER'S

Bowl of cold turkie fool
A roast chicken liver louie
My cigarillo's going out in a spanish bedroom
Jazz is for free
Coke is for free
Junk's unlimited and sold by Agents
  that I can make poems that I spin the day to
  Tim Buck Two that I lose tension and head
  floats forever a far inscape of lemon trees AND
NO MORE REALITY SANDWICHES!!!

Can I ever get up from this table?
Can I ever stop thunder?
Can I make it to windows of fur?
Can I soup up her eyes in a can of star milk and shoot it for
        light?

Can I read in the park?
Can I sit on the Moon? Can I?

Oh, stop it! Oh start! Oh, make music
Though your arm is too thin
  and the jails are too small, sweaty AND STINK!

TULI KUPFERBERG

GREENWICH VILLAGE OF MY DREAMS

A rose in a stone.
Chariots on the West Side Highway.
Blues in the Soviet Union.
Onions in times square.
A Japanese in Chinatown.
A soup sandwich.
A Hudson terraplane.
Chess in a Catskill bungalow.
Awnings in Atlanta.
Lewisohn stadium in the blackout.
Brooklyn beneath the East River.
      the waves passover.
The Battery in startling sunlight.
Kleins in Ohrbachs.
Love on the dole, Roosevelt not elected.
Hoover under the 3rd Ave El
Joe Gould kissing Maxwell Bodenheim
      & puffing on his pipe
Edna Millay feeling Edmund Wilson
Charlie Parker & Ted Joans talking
      in Sheridan Sq Park & its cold man!
The Cedar St Bar with Cedars in it
      & autos crashing against the cedars
The Chase Manhattan Bank closed
      down for repairs. To open as the
      new Waldorf Cafeteria.
Lionel Trilling kissing Allen Ginsberg
      after great Reading in the Gaslight

The Limelight changes its name to
    the Electric Light & features
    Charlie Chaplin as a s(w)inging
    waiter
Edgar Allan Poe becoming the dentist
    in the Waverly dispensary & giving
    everyone free nitrous oxide high
Louis getting thrown out of Louis'
San Remo stepping up to the bar &
    asking for a wet Martini
The Charleston on Charles St
    featuring my Sister Eileen
    & the Kronstadt sailors.
Max Eastman & John Reed
    buying Gungawala hashish candy
    at the German Delicatessen on 6th
    Ave & West 4th Street.
Tourists bringing pictures to sell
    to artists in their annual disposition.
Civilians telling cops to move on
Coffeehouses that sell brandy
    in their coffee cups
Eugene O'Neill insisting on coffee
John Barrymore in offbroadway Hamlet
Walt Whitman cruising on MacDougal
Ike & Mamie drunk in Minettas
Khrushchev singing peat bog soldiers
    in the circle (with a balalaika)
Everybody kissing & hugging squeezing
Khrushchev & Eisenhower a big fat kiss
The world an art
Life a joy
The village come to life again

I wake up singing
I that dwell in New York
Sweet song bless my mouth
Beauty bless my eyes

Song of the world
Fly forth from dreams!

How beautiful is love
And the fruit thereof
Holy holy holy
A kiss and a star

SALLY STERN

WAIT, I'VE BEEN THIS WAY BEFORE

Wait
I've been this way before.
I know these shapes
And textures under blind fingers.

I know that I shall be the sea
And the mother
And never me.
Wait
I am here
Under the sea
Recognize me.

Tongue tempted, teased
You reach, breathing
To break like sky-fires
In an inward breath
And then you kiss my mouth,
Then.
And rest
Like a child suckling
In its innocence.

All right it's not me
It's the mother and the sea.

DAN PROPPER

AFTERNOON

Asleep
you are a different person:
the chinablue-eyed
Modigliani-long-hot-catlike
you
relaxes
into a womanshadowed girl,
warm, curled-up,
the soft sigh of your breath
issuing . . .

I stand
over your bed
—I want to gently embrace
your tiny perfect form,
kiss your forehead,
kiss your cheek
—yet I am afraid
of waking you.

LeROI JONES

EPISTROPHE (FOR YODO)

It's such a static reference; looking
out the window all the time! the eyes' limits . . .
On good days, the sun.

& what you see. (here in New York)
Walls and buildings; or in the hidden gardens
of opulent Queens: profusion, endless stretches of leisure.

It's like being chained to some dead actress;
& she keeps trying to tell you something horribly maudlin.

e.g.
    ('the leaves are flat & motionless.')

What I know of the mind
seems to end here;
Just outside my face.

I wish some weird looking animal
would come along.

PROSE

ALLEN GINSBERG

FROM JOURNALS (1957)

Dream

Great floods in Paterson. I get home—Lucien around?—copies
of N.Y. Times—edited by Bill Burroughs—
     Belgrade rebels, area Communist (I thought of extent of
inner corruption)—middle area of Yugoslavia in doubt.
     Also a headline

> WORLD IN FLOOD WATER
> EVERYWHERE ETC. PAPER GOES
> ON. BURROUGHS AT HELM, ETC.
>   —a joke headline—

inside a paper with mimeographed list of subscribers? or possible future co-workers on paper.

* * *

     Don't forget evening party at which had X, Kingsland,
Dick Howard, Carl & Olive—Y drunkenly riding uptown for
liquor—X hurt in small smash, cursing doctors over phone,
then Y & X necking, ripping X's fly open, her sucking his
white dick, pallid, and her posture of arched back & readiness
on his knees, him with hand in her crotch—and their
conversation—'I'm as nasty as you'—
     Y: 'I love you for your nastiness'—and 'You're a silly girl'—
and me sleeping with her later at her place.

* * *

The Wisdom of Solomon (Carl)

     They censor words not the things they denote:
          It would create less of a stir to drop a piece of shit
     on Grant's tomb
               than to write it out in white paint.

Because people recognize that's what memorials are for—old bums & dogs to shit on.

Act boldly, think with Caution—even timorously

* * *

A Novel

At 14 I was an introvert, an atheist, a Communist and a Jew, and I still wanted to be president of the United States.

At 19, being no longer a virgin, I was a cocksucker, and believed in a supreme reality, an anarchist, a hipster totally apolitical Reichian; I wanted to be a great poet instead.

At 22 I was a hallucinating mystic believing in the City of God and I wanted to be a saint.

At 23, a year later, I was already a criminal, a despairing sinner, a dope fiend; I wanted to get to reality.

At 24, after being a jailbird, a schizoid screwball in the bughouse, I got layed, girls, I was being psychoanalyzed.

At 26, I am shy, go out with girls, I write poetry, I am a freelance literary agent and a registered democrat; I want to find a job.
Who cares?

* * *

Crazy—A Magazine
Issue on Cannastra; Joan, Kammerer.

* * *

Up from my books.
The moon in the window,
Summer night and solid sky.

Black hollow of buildings,
A hundred different chimneys.
I see lit windows but no humans to watch.

June 17, 1952

Limping down the block, foot bruised yesterday in peyote euphoria on Washington Sq. with Keck & Anton.*

A boy came out of Shelley's, early twenties, in dungarees & striped T shirt—carrying 2 glasses of red liquor walking in front of me.

I sit naked in my room remembering the animal swing of his buttocks, the length and strength and paleness of his arms in the darkness as he balanced his way brushing slightly drunken against the granite of the building with his arm.

It is midnight in the blue attic, summer, a thin film of sweat on my face.

He stopped after walking the length of the building down the sidestreet in the darkness, by an iron fence which led to an iron stairway down to a cement courtyard behind the building.

He put both glasses down, bending over—were they filled with wine—picked one up, and drank it all straight down. I walked on, staring back, he looked at me and said—

'I got a good deal out of the bar,' or something.

'What a way to drink!' I said incoherently, walking on. I wanted to stop and make him—thinking of the crowd of youths around the pinball machine in the bar 2 months ago, the hunchback, the handsome one, the other boys—afraid of being discovered on the block as a queer, or afraid of him & afraid to stop & talk. He was quite tall and evenly formed.

This reminds me—he not a great face, just another momentary sadness of unobtainable common beauty—of the truly great strangers, the appearances of majesty I have seen on the streets here and there. A project which I have meant to sketch for several weeks.

In Houston, 1948—I was broke, stealing Pepsi Cola bottles

*'Keck & Anton: members of a circle of seekers, some from West Coast, friends of Philip Lamantia & Carl Solomon, who hung around San Remo Bar, MacDougal & Bleecker, Greenwich Village, at that time a center of Kerouac's N.Y. social life—described in *The Subterraneans*, late 40's & early 50's.'—A. G., September 1975.

to cash in and buy candy bars for hunger, waiting for a ship. Outside the old Union Hall, walking down the street, a Latin animal, Cuban, Spanish, I don't know. Electricity seemed to flow from his powerful body—black hair, curled wildly, looked impossible for him to live in society, to me—powerful malignant features—he was perhaps 22 or less—springing down the street in a tense potent walk, dungarees, powerful legs, not too tall, blue shirt opened several buttons on the chest, black hair curling sparsely on chest—he seemed made of iron, no sweat—or brown polished rock. I never in my life saw a more perfect being—expression of vigor and potency and natural rage on face—I couldn't conceive of him speaking English. I wonder what loves he had. Who could resist him? He must have taken any weak body he needed or wanted. Love from such a face I could not imagine, nor gentleness—but love and gentleness are not needed where there was so much life. He just passed me by and I stood there amazed staring at him as he disappeared up the block & around the corner scattering the air in spiritual waves behind him. I couldn't believe he was human. He had thick features, black eyebrows, almost square face, powerful chest, perfect freedom of walk.

JACK KEROUAC

110 M.P.H. AND THE AMERICAN BOP NIGHT*

In no time at all we were back on the main highway and that night I saw the entire state of Nebraska unroll before my eyes. A hundred and ten miles an hour straight through, an arrow road, sleeping towns, no traffic, and the Union Pacific streamliner falling behind us in the moonlight. I wasn't frightened at all that night; it was perfectly legitimate to go 110 and talk and have all the Nebraska towns—Ogallala, Gothenburg, Kearney, Grand Island, Columbus—unreel with dreamlike rapidity as we roared ahead and talked. It was a magnificent car; it could hold the road like a boat holds on water. Gradual curves were its singing ease. 'Ah, man, what a dreamboat,' sighed Dean. 'Think if you and I had a car like this what we could do. Do you know there's a road that goes down Mexico and all the way to Panama?—and maybe all the way to the bottom of South America where the Indians are seven feet tall and eat cocaine on the mountainside? Yes! You and I, Sal, we'd dig the whole world with a car like this because, man, the road must eventually lead to the whole world. Ain't nowhere else it can go—right? Oh, and are we going to cut around old Chi with this thing! Think of it, Sal, I've never been to Chicago in all my life, never stopped.'

'We'll come in there like gangsters in this Cadillac!'

'Yes! And girls! We can pick up girls, in fact, Sal, I've decided to make extra-special fast time so we can have an entire evening to cut around in this thing. Now you just relax and I'll ball the jack all the way.'

'Well, how fast are you going now?'

'A steady one-ten I figure—you wouldn't notice it. We've still got all Iowa in the daytime and then I'll make that old Illinois in nothing flat.' The boys fell asleep and we talked and talked all night.

*Chapters 9, 10 and 11 of *On the Road*.

It was remarkable how Dean could go mad and then suddenly continue with his soul—which I think is wrapped up in a fast car, a coast to reach, and a woman at the end of the road—calmly and sanely as though nothing had happened. 'I get like that every time in Denver now—I can't make that town any more. Gookly, gooky, Dean's a spooky. Zoom!' I told him I had been over this Nebraska road before in '47. He had too. 'Sal, when I was working for the New Era Laundry in Los Angeles, nineteen forty-four, falsifying my age, I made a trip to Indianapolis Speedway for the express purpose of seeing the Memorial Day classic hitch, hiking by day and stealing cars by night to make time. Also I had a twenty-dollar Buick back in LA, my first car, it couldn't pass the brake and light inspection so I decided I needed an out-of-state license to operate the car without arrest so went through here to get the license. As I was hitchhiking through one of these very towns, with the plates concealed under my coat, a nosy sheriff who thought I was pretty young to be hitchhiking accosted me on the main drag. He found the plates and threw me in the two-cell jail with a county delinquent who should have been in the home for the old since he couldn't feed himself (the sheriff's wife fed him) and sat through the day drooling and slobbering. After investigation, which included corny things like a fatherly quiz, then an abrupt turnabout to frighten me with threats, a comparison of my handwriting, et cetera, and after I made the most magnificent speech of my life to get out of it, concluding with the confession that I was lying about my car-stealing past and was only looking for my paw who was a farmhand hereabouts, he let me go. Of course I missed the races. The following fall I did the same thing again to see the Notre Dame–California game in South Bend, Indiana—trouble none this time and, Sal, I had just the money for the ticket and not an extra cent and didn't eat anything all up and back except for what I could panhandle from all kinds of crazy cats I met on the road and at the same time gun gals. Only guy in the United States of America that ever went to so much trouble to see a ball-game.'

I asked him the circumstances of his being in LA in 1944.

'I was arrested in Arizona, the joint absolutely the worst joint I've ever been in. I had to escape and pulled the greatest escape in my life, speaking of escapes, you see, in a general way. In the woods, you know, and crawling, and swamps—up around that mountain country. Rubber hoses and the works and accidental so-called death facing me I had to cut out of those woods along the ridge so as to keep away from trails and paths and roads. Had to get rid of my joint clothes and sneaked the neatest theft of a shirt and pants from a gas station outside Flagstaff, arriving LA two days later clad as gas attendant and walked to the first station I saw and got hired and got myself a room and changed name (Lee Buliay) and spent an exciting year in LA, including a whole gang of new friends and some really great girls, that season ending when we were all driving on Hollywood Boulevard one night and I told my buddy to steer the car while I kissed my girl—I was at the wheel, see—and *he didn't hear me* and we ran smack into a post but only going twenty and I broke my nose. You've seen before my nose—the crooked Grecian curve up here. After that I went to Denver and met Marylou in a soda fountain that spring. Oh, man, she was only fifteen and wearing jeans and just waiting for someone to pick her up. Three days three nights of talk in the Ace Hotel, third floor, southeast corner room, holy memento room and sacred scene of my days—she was so sweet then, so *young*, hmm, ahh! But hey, look down there in the night thar, hup, hup, a buncha old bums by a fire by the rail, damn me.' He almost slowed down. 'You see, I never know whether my father's there or not.' There were some figures by the tracks, reeling in front of a woodfire. 'I never know whether to ask. He might be anywhere.' We drove on. Somewhere behind us or in front of us in the huge night his father lay drunk under a bush, and no doubt about it—spittle on his chin, water on his pants, molasses in his ears, scabs on his nose, maybe blood in his hair and the moon shining down on him.

I took Dean's arm. 'Ah, man, we're sure going home now.' New York was going to be his permanent home for the first time. He jiggled all over; he couldn't wait.

'And think, Sal, when we get to Pennsy we'll start hearing that gone Eastern bop on the disk jockeys. Geeyah, roll, old boat, roll!' The magnificent car made the wind roar; it made the plains unfold like a roll of paper; it cast hot tar from itself with deference—an imperial boat. I opened my eyes to a fanning dawn; we were hurling up to it. Dean's rocky dogged face as ever bent over the dashlight with a bony purpose of its own.

'What are you thinking, Pops?'

'Ah-ha, ah-ha, same old thing, y'know—gurls gurls gurls.'

I went to sleep and woke up to the dry, hot atmosphere of July Sunday morning in Iowa, and still Dean was driving and driving and had not slackened his speed; he took the curvy corndales of Iowa at a minimum of eighty and the straightaway 110 as usual, unless both-ways traffic forced him to fall in line at a crawling and miserable sixty. When there was a chance he shot ahead and passed cars by the half-dozen and left them behind in a cloud of dust. A mad guy in a brand-new Buick saw all this on the road and decided to race us. When Dean was just about to pass a passel the guy shot by us without warning and howled and tooted his horn and flashed the tail lights for challenge. We took off after him like a big bird. 'Now wait,' laughed Dean, 'I'm going to tease that sonofabitch for a dozen miles or so. Watch.' He let the Buick go way ahead and then accelerated and caught up with it most impolitely. Mad Buick went out of his mind; he gunned up to a hundred. We had a chance to see who he was. He seemed to be some kind of Chicago hipster traveling with a woman old enough to be—and probably actually was—his mother. God knows if she was complaining, but he raced. His hair was dark and wild, an Italian from old Chi; he wore a sports shirt. Maybe there was an idea in his mind that we were a new gang from LA invading Chicago, maybe some of Mickey Cohen's men, because the limousine looked every bit the part and the license plates were California. Mainly it was just road kicks. He took terrible chances to stay ahead of us; he passed cars on curves and barely got back in line as a truck wobbled into view and loomed up huge. Eighty miles of Iowa we unreeled in this fashion, and the race was so interesting that I had no opportunity to be frightened. Then the mad guy gave up, pulled up at a gas station, probably on orders from the old lady, and as we roared by he waved gleefully. On we sped, Dean barechested, I with my feet on the dashboard, and the college boys sleeping in the back. We stopped to eat breakfast at a diner run by a white-haired lady who gave us extra-large portions of potatoes as churchbells rang in the nearby town. Then off again.

'Dean, don't drive so fast in the daytime.'

'Don't worry, man, I know what I'm doing.' I began to flinch. Dean came up on lines of cars like the Angel of Terror. He almost rammed them along as he looked for an opening. He teased their bumpers, he eased and pushed and craned around to see the curve, then the huge car leaped to his touch and passed, and always by a hair we made it back to our side as other lines filed by in the opposite direction and I shuddered. I couldn't take it any more. It is only seldom that you find a long Nebraskan straightaway in Iowa, and when we finally hit one Dean made his usual 110 and I saw flashing by outside several scenes that I remembered from 1947—a long stretch where Eddie and I had been stranded two hours. All that old road of the past unreeling dizzily as if the cup of life had been overturned and everything gone mad. My eyes ached in nightmare day.

'Ah hell, Dean, I'm going in the back seat, I can't stand it any more, I can't look.'

'Hee-hee-hee!' tittered Dean and he passed a car on a narrow bridge and swerved in dust and roared on. I jumped in the back seat and curled up to sleep. One of the boys jumped in front for the fun. Great horrors that we were going to crash this very morning took hold of me and I got down on the floor and closed my eyes and tried to go to sleep. As a seaman I used to think of the waves rushing beneath the shell of the ship and the bottomless deeps thereunder—now I could feel the road some twenty inches beneath me, unfurling and flying and hissing at incredible speeds across the groaning continent with that mad Ahab at the wheel. When I closed my eyes all I could see was the road unwinding into me. When I opened them I saw flashing shadows of trees vibrating on the floor of the car. There was no escaping it. I resigned myself to all. And still Dean drove, he had no thought of sleeping till we got to Chicago. In the afternoon we crossed old Des Moines again. Here of course we got snarled in traffic and had to go slow and I got back in the front seat. A strange pathetic accident took place. A fat colored man was driving with his entire family in a sedan in front of us; on the rear bumper hung one of those canvas desert waterbags they sell tourists in the desert. He pulled up sharp, Dean was talking to the boys in the back and didn't notice, and we rammed him at five miles an hour smack on the waterbag, which burst like a boil and squirted water in the air. No other damage except a bent bumper. Dean and I got out to talk to him. The upshot of it was an exchange of addresses and some talk, and Dean not taking his eyes off the man's wife whose beautiful brown breasts were barely concealed inside a floppy cotton blouse. 'Yass, yass,' We gave him the address of our Chicago baron and went on.

The other side of Des Moines a cruising car came after us with the siren growling, with orders to pull over. 'Now what?'

The cop came out. 'Were you in an accident coming in?'

'Accident? We broke a guy's waterbag at the junction.'

'He says he was hit and run by a bunch in a stolen car.' This was one of the few instances Dean and I knew of a Negro's acting like a suspicious old fool. It so surprised us we laughed. We had to follow the patrolman to the station and there spent an hour waiting in the grass while they telephoned Chicago to get the owner of the Cadillac and verify our position as hired drivers. Mr. Baron said, according to the cop, 'Yes, that is my car but I can't vouch for anything else those boys might have done.'

'They were in a minor accident here in Des Moines.'

'Yes, you've already told me that—what I meant was, I can't vouch for anything they might have done in the past.'

Everything was straightened out and we roared on. Newton, Iowa, it was, where I'd taken that dawn walk in 1947. In the afternoon we crossed drowsy old Davenport again and the low-lying Mississippi in her sawdust bed; then Rock Island, a few minutes of traffic, the sun reddening, and sudden sights of lovely little tributary rivers flowing softly among the magic trees and greeneries of mid-American Illinois. It was beginning to look like the soft sweet East again; the great dry West was accomplished and done. The state of Illinois unfolded before my eyes in one vast movement that lasted a matter of hours as Dean balled straight across at the same speed. In his tiredness he was taking greater chances than ever. At a narrow bridge that crossed one of these lovely little rivers he shot precipitately into an almost impossible situation. Two slow cars ahead of us were bumping over the bridge; coming the other way was a huge truck-trailer with a driver who was making a close estimate of how long it would take the slow cars to negotiate the bridge, and his estimate was that by the time he got there they'd be over. There was absolutely no room on the bridge for the truck and any cars going the other direction. Behind the truck cars pulled out and peeked for a chance to get by it. In front of the slow cars other slow cars were pushing along. The road was crowded and everyone exploding to pass. Dean came down on all this at 110 miles an hour and never hesitated. He passed the slow cars, swerved, and almost hit the left rail of the bridge, went head-on into the shadow of the unslowing truck, cut right sharply, just missed the truck's left front wheel, almost hit the first slow car, pulled out to pass, and then had to cut back in line when another car came out from behind the truck to look, all in a matter of two seconds, flashing by and leaving nothing more than a cloud of dust instead of a horrible five-way crash with cars lurching in every direction and the great truck humping its back in the fatal red afternoon of Illinois with its dreaming fields. I couldn't get it out of my mind, also, that a famous bop clarinetist had died in an Illinois car-crash recently, probably on a day like this. I went to the back seat again.

The boys stayed in the back too now. Dean was bent on Chicago before nightfall. At a road-rail junction we picked up two hobos who rounded up a half-buck between them for gas. A moment before sitting around piles of railroad ties, polishing off the last of some wine, now they found themselves in a muddy but unbowed and splendid Cadillac limousine headed for Chicago in precipitous haste. In fact the old boy up front who sat next to Dean never took his eyes off the road and prayed his poor bum prayers, I tell you. 'Well,' they said, 'we never knew we'd get to Chicaga sa fast.' As we passed drowsy Illinois towns where the people are so conscious of Chicago gangs that pass like this in limousines every day, we were a strange sight: all of us unshaven, the driver barechested, two bums, myself in the back seat, holding on to a strap and my head leaned back on the cushion looking at the countryside with an imperious eye—just like a new California gang come to contest the spoils of Chicago, a band of desperados escaped from the prisons of the Utah moon. When we stopped for Cokes and gas at a small-town station people came out to stare at us but they never said a word and I think made mental notes of our descriptions and heights in case of future need. To transact business with the girl who ran the gas-pump Dean merely threw on his T-shirt like a scarf and was curt and abrupt as usual and got back in the car and off we roared again. Pretty soon the redness turned purple, the last of the enchanted rivers flashed by, and we saw distant smokes of Chicago beyond the drive. We had come from Denver to Chicago via Ed Wall's ranch, 1180 miles, in exactly seventeen hours, not counting the two hours in the ditch and three at the ranch and two with the police in Newton, Iowa, for a mean average of seventy miles per hour across the land, with one driver. Which is a kind of crazy record.

* * *

Great Chicago glowed red before our eyes. We were suddenly on Madison Street among hordes of hobos, some of them sprawled out on the street with their feet on the curb, hundreds of others milling in the doorways of saloons and alleys. 'Wup! wup! look sharp for old Dean Moriarty there, he may be in Chicago by accident this year.' We let out the hobos on this street and proceeded to downtown Chicago. Screeching trolleys, newsboys, gals cutting by, the smell of fried food and beer in the air, neons winking—'We're in the big town, Sal!

Whooee!' First thing to do was park the Cadillac in a good dark spot and wash up and dress for the night. Across the street from the YMCA we found a red-brick alley between buildings, where we stashed the Cadillac with her snout pointed to the street and ready to go, then followed the college boys up to the Y, where they got a room and allowed us to use their facilities for an hour. Dean and I shaved and showered, I dropped my wallet in the hall, Dean found it and was about to sneak it in his shirt when he realized it was ours and was right disappointed. Then we said goodbye to those boys, who were glad they'd made it in one piece, and took off to eat in a cafeteria. Old brown Chicago with the strange semi-Eastern, semi-Western types going to work and spitting. Dean stood in the cafeteria rubbing his belly and taking it all in. He wanted to talk to a strange middle-aged colored woman who had come into the cafeteria with a story about how she had no money but she had buns with her and would they give her butter. She came in flapping her hips, was turned down, and went out flipping her butt. 'Whoo!' said Dean. 'Let's follow her down the street, let's take her to the ole Cadillac in the alley. We'll have a ball.' But we forgot that and headed straight for North Clark Street, after a spin in the Loop, to see the hootchy-kootchy joints and hear the bop. And what a night it was. 'Oh, man,' said Dean to me as we stood in front of a bar, 'dig the street of life, the Chinamen that cut by in Chicago. What a weird town—wow, and that woman in that window up there, just looking down with her big breasts hanging from her night-gown, big wide eyes. Whee. Sal, we gotta go and never stop going till we get there.'

'Where we going, man?'

'I don't know but we gotta go.' Then here came a gang of young bop musicians carrying their instruments out of cars. They piled right into a saloon and we followed them. They set themselves up and started blowing. There we were! The leader was a slender, drooping, curly-haired, pursy-mouthed tenorman, thin of shoulder, draped loose in a sports shirt, cool in the warm night, self-indulgence written in his eyes, who picked up his horn and frowned in it and blew cool and complex and was dainty stamping his foot to catch ideas, and ducked to miss others—and said, 'Blow,' very quietly when the other boys took solos. Then there was Prez, a husky, handsome blond like a freckled boxer, meticulously wrapped inside his sharkskin plaid suit with the long drape and the collar falling back and the tie undone for exact sharpness and casualness, sweating and hitching up his horn and writhing into it, and a tone just like Lester Young himself. 'You see, man, Prez has the technical anxieties of a money-making musician, he's the only one who's well dressed, see him grow worried when he blows a clinker, but the leader, that cool cat, tells him not to worry and just blow and blow—the mere sound and serious exuberance of the music is all *he* cares about. He's an artist. He's teaching young Prez the boxer. Now the others dig!!' The third sax was an alto, eighteen-year-old cool, contemplative young Charlie-Parker-type Negro from high school, with a broadgash mouth, taller than the rest, grave. He raised his horn and blew into it quietly and thoughtfully and elicited birdlike phrases and architectural Miles Davis logics. These were the children of the great bop innovators.

Once there was Louis Armstrong blowing his beautiful top in the muds of New Orleans; before him the mad musicians who had paraded on official days and broke up their Sousa marches into ragtime. Then there was swing, and Roy Eldridge, vigorous and virile, blasting the horn for everything it had in waves of power and logic and subtlety—leaning to it with glittering eyes and a lovely smile and sending it out broadcast to rock the jazz world. Then had come Charlie Parker, a kid in his mother's woodshed in Kansas City, blowing his taped-up alto among the logs, practicing on rainy days, coming out to watch the old swinging Basie and Benny Moten band that had Hot Lips Page and the rest—Charlie Parker leaving home and coming to Harlem, and meeting mad Thelonius Monk and madder Gillespie—Charlie Parker in his early days when he was flipped and walked around in a circle while playing. Somewhat younger than Lester Young, also from KC, that gloomy, saintly goof in whom the history of jazz was wrapped; for when he held his horn high and horizontal from his mouth he blew the greatest; and as his hair grew longer and he got lazier and stretched-out, his horn came down halfway; till it finally fell all the way and today as he wears his thick-soled shoes so that he can't feel the sidewalks of life his horn is held weakly against his chest, and he blows cool and easy getout phrases. Here were the children of the American bop night.

Stranger flowers yet—for as the Negro alto mused over everyone's head with dignity, the young, tall, slender, blond kid from Curtis Street, Denver, jeans and studded belt, sucked on his mouthpiece while waiting for the others to finish; and when they did he started, and you had to look around to see where the solo was coming from, for it came from angelical smiling lips upon the mouthpiece and it was a soft, sweet, fairy-tale solo on an alto. Lonely as America, a throatpierced sound in the night.

What of the others and all the soundmaking? There was the bass-player, wiry redhead with wild eyes, jabbing his hips at the fiddle with every driving slap, at hot moments his mouth hanging open trancelike. 'Man, there's a cat who can really *bend* his girl!' The sad drummer, like our white hipster in Frisco Folsom Street, completely goofed, staring into space, chewing gum, wide-eyed, rocking the neck with Reich kick and complacent estasy. The piano—a big husky Italian truck-driving kid with meaty hands, a burly and thoughtful joy. They played an hour. Nobody was listening. Old North Clark bums lolled at the bar, whores screeched in anger. Secret Chinamen went by. Noises of hootchy-kootchy interfered. They went right on. Out on the sidewalk came an apparition—a sixteen-year-old kid with a goatee and a trombone case. Thin as rickets, mad-faced, he wanted to join this group and blow with them. They knew him and didn't want to bother with him. He crept into the bar and surreptitiously undid his trombone and raised it to his lips. No opening. Nobody looked at him. They finished, packed up, and left for another bar. He wanted to jump, skinny Chicago kid. He slapped on his dark glasses, raised the trombone to his lips alone in the bar, and went 'Baugh!' Then he rushed out after them. They wouldn't let him play with them, just like the sandlot football team in back of the gas tank. 'All these guys live with their grandmothers just like Tom Snark and our Carlo Marx alto,' said Dean. We rushed after the whole gang. They went into Anita O'Day's club and there unpacked and played till nine o'clock in the morning. Dean and I were there with beers.

At intermissions we rushed out in the Cadillac and tried to pick up girls all up and down Chicago. They were frightened of our big, scarred, prophetic car. In his mad frenzy Dean backed up smack on hydrants and tittered maniacally. By nine o'clock the car was an utter wreck; the brakes weren't working any more; the fenders were stove in; the rods were rattling. Dean couldn't stop it at red lights, it kept kicking convulsively over the roadway. It had paid the price of the night. It was a muddy boot and no longer a shiny limousine. 'Whee!' The boys were still blowing at Neets'.

Suddenly Dean stared into the darkness of a corner beyond the bandstand and said, 'Sal, God has arrived.'

I looked. *George Shearing*. And as always he leaned his blind head on his pale hand, all ears opened like the ears of an elephant, listening to the American sounds and mastering them for his own English summer's-night use. Then they urged him to get up and play. He did. He played innumerable choruses with amazing chords that mounted higher and higher till the sweat splashed all over the piano and everybody listened in awe and fright. They led him off the stand after an hour. He went back to his dark corner, old God Shearing, and the boys said, 'There ain't nothin left after that.'

But the slender leader frowned. 'Let's blow anyway.'

Something would come of it yet. There's always more, a little further—it never ends. They sought to find new phrases after Shearing's explorations; they tried hard. They writhed and twisted and blew. Every now and then a clear harmonic cry gave new suggestions of a tune that would someday be the only tune in the world and would raise men's souls to joy. They found it, they lost, they wrestled for it, they found it again, they laughed, they moaned—and Dean sweated at the table and told them to go, go, go. At nine o'clock in the morning everybody—musicians, girls in slacks, bartenders, and the one little skinny, unhappy trombonist—staggered out of the club into the great roar of Chicago day to sleep until the wild bop night again.

Dean and I shuddered in the raggedness. It was now time to return the Cadillac to the owner, who lived out on Lake Shore Drive in a swank apartment with an enormous garage underneath managed by oil-scarred Negroes. We drove out there and swung the muddy heap into its berth. The mechanic did not recognize the Cadillac. We handed the papers over. He scratched his head at the sight of it. We had to get out fast. We did. We took a bus back to downtown Chicago and that was that. And we never heard a word from our Chicago baron about the condition of his car, in spite of the fact that he had our addresses and could have complained.

* * *

It was time for us to move on. We took a bus to Detroit. Our money was now running quite low. We lugged our wretched baggage through the station. By now Dean's thumb bandage was almost as black as coal and all unrolled. We were both as miserable-looking as anybody could be after all the things we'd done. Exhausted, Dean fell asleep in the bus that roared across the state of Michigan. I took up a conversation with a gorgeous country girl wearing a low-cut cotton blouse that displayed the beautiful sun-tan on her breast tops. She was dull. She spoke of evenings in the country making popcorn on the porch. Once this would have gladdened my heart but because her heart was not glad when she said it I knew there was nothing in it but the idea of what one should do. 'And what else do you do for fun?' I tried to bring up boy friends and sex. Her great dark eyes surveyed me with emptiness and a kind of chagrin that reached back generations and generations in her blood from not having done what was crying to be done—whatever it was, and everybody knows what it was. 'What do you want out of life?' I wanted to take her and wring it out of her. She didn't have the slightest idea what she wanted. She mumbled of jobs, movies, going to her grandmother's for the summer, wishing she could go to New York and visit the Roxy, what kind of outfit she would wear—something like the one she wore last Easter, white bonnet, roses, rose pumps, and lavender gabardine coat. 'What do you do on Sunday afternoons?' I asked. She sat on her porch. The boys went by on bicycles and stopped to chat. She read the funny papers, she reclined on the hammock. 'What do you do on a warm summer's night?' She sat on the porch, she watched the cars in the road. She and her mother made popcorn. 'What does your father do on a summer's night?' He works, he has an all-night shift at the boiler factory, he's spent his whole life supporting a woman and her outpoppings and no credit or adoration. 'What does your brother do on a summer's night?' He rides around on his bicycle, he hangs out in front of the soda fountain. 'What is he aching to do? What are we all aching to do? What do we want?' She didn't know. She yawned. She was sleepy. It was too much. Nobody could tell. Nobody would ever tell. It was all over. She was eighteen and most lovely, and lost.

And Dean and I, ragged and dirty as if we had lived off locust, stumbled out of the bus in Detroit. We decided to stay up in all-night movies on Skid Row. It was too cold for parks. Hassel had been here on Detroit Skid Row, he had dug every shooting gallery and all-night movie and every brawling bar with his dark eyes many a time. His ghost haunted us. We'd never find him on Times Square again. We thought maybe by accident Old Dean Moriarty was here too—but he was not. For thirty-five cents each we went into the beat-up old movie and sat down in the balcony till morning, when we were shooed downstairs. The people who were in that all-night movie were the end. Beat Negroes who'd come up from Alabama to work in car factories on a rumor; old white bums; young longhaired hipsters who'd reached the end of the road and were drinking wine; whores, ordinary couples, and housewives with nothing to do, nowhere to go, nobody to believe in. If you sifted all Detroit in a wire basket the beater solid core of dregs couldn't be better gathered. The picture was Singing Cowboy Eddie Dean and his gallant white horse Bloop, that was number one; number two double-feature film was George Raft, Sidney

Greenstreet, and Peter Lorre in a picture about Istanbul. We
saw both of these things six times each during the night. We
saw them waking, we heard them sleeping, we sensed them
dreaming, we were permeated completely with the strange
Gray Myth of the West and the weird dark Myth of the East
when morning came. All my actions since then have been
dictated automatically to my subconscious by this horrible
osmotic experience. I heard big Greenstreet sneer a hundred
times; I heard Peter Lorre make his sinister come-on; I was
with George Raft in his paranoiac fears; I rode and sang with
Eddie Dean and shot up the rustlers innumerable times.
People slugged out of bottles and turned around and looked
everywhere in the dark theater for something to do, somebody
to talk to. In the head everybody was guiltily quiet, nobody
talked. In the gray dawn that puffed ghostlike about the
windows of the theater and hugged its eaves I was sleeping
with my head on the wooden arm of a seat as six attendants of
the theater converged with their night's total of swept-up
rubbish and created a huge dusty pile that reached to my nose
as I snored head down—till they almost swept me away too.
This was reported to me by Dean, who was watching from ten
seats behind. All the cigarette butts, the bottles, the match-
books, the come and the gone were swept up in this pile. Had
they taken me with it, Dean would never have seen me again.
He would have had to roam the entire United States and look
in every garbage pail from coast to coast before he found me
embryonically convoluted among the rubbishes of my life, his
life, and the life of everybody concerned and not concerned.
What would I have said to him from my rubbish womb? 'Don't
bother me, man, I'm happy where I am. You lost me one night
in Detroit in August nineteen forty-nine. What right have you
to come and disturb my reverie in this pukish can?' In 1942 I
was the star in one of the filthiest dramas of all time. I was a
seaman, and went to the Imperial Café on Scollay Square in
Boston to drink; I drank sixty glasses of beer and retired to the
toilet, where I wrapped myself around the toilet bowl and went
to sleep. During the night at least a hundred seamen and
assorted civilians came in and cast their sentient debouchments

on me till I was unrecognizably caked. What difference does it make after all?—anonymity in the world of men is better than fame in heaven; for what's heaven? what's earth? All in the mind.

Gibberishly Dean and I stumbled out of this horror-hole at dawn and went to find our travel-bureau car. After spending a good part of the morning in Negro bars and chasing gals and listening to jazz records on jukeboxes, we struggled five miles in local buses with all our crazy gear and got to the home of a man who was going to charge us four dollars apiece for the ride to New York. He was a middle-aged blond fellow with glasses, with a wife and kid and a good home. We waited in the yard while he got ready. His lovely wife in cotton kitchen dress offered us coffee but we were too busy talking. By this time Dean was so exhausted and out of his mind that everything he saw delighted him. He was reaching another pious frenzy. He sweated and sweated. The moment we were in the new Chrysler and off to New York the poor man realized he had contracted a ride with two maniacs, but he made the best of it and in fact got used to us just as we passed Briggs Stadium and talked about next year's Detroit Tigers.

In the misty night we crossed Toledo and went onward across old Ohio. I realized I was beginning to cross and re-cross towns in America as though I were a traveling salesman—raggedy travelings, bad stock, rotten beans in the bottom of my bag of tricks, nobody buying. The man got tired near Pennsylvania and Dean took the wheel and drove clear the rest of the way to New York, and we began to hear the Symphony Sid show on the radio with all the latest bop, and now we were entering the great and final city of America. We got there in early morning. Times Square was being torn up, for New York never rests. We looked for Hassel automatically as we passed.

In an hour Dean and I were out at my aunt's new flat in Long Island, and she herself was busily engaged with painters who were friends of the family, and arguing with them about the price as we stumbled up the stairs from San Francisco. 'Sal,' said my aunt, 'Dean can stay here a few days and after that he has to get out, do you understand me?' The trip was over. Dean and I took a walk that night among the gas tanks and railroad bridges and fog lamps of Long Island. I remember him standing under a streetlamp.

'Just as we passed that other lamp I was going to tell you a further thing, Sal, but now I am parenthetically continuing with a new thought and by the time we reach the next I'll return to the original subject, agreed?' I certainly agreed. We were so used to traveling we had to walk all over Long Island, but there was no more land, just the Atlantic Ocean, and we could only go so far. We clasped hands and agreed to be friends forever.

Not five nights later we went to a party in New York and I saw a girl called Inez and told her I had a friend with me that she ought to meet sometime. I was drunk and told her he was a cowboy. 'Oh, I've always wanted to meet a cowboy.'

'Dean?' I yelled across the party—which included Angel Luz García, the poet; Walter Evans; Victor Villanueva, the Venezuelan poet; Jinny Jones, a former love of mine; Carlo Marx; Gene Dexter; and innumerable others—'Come over here, man.' Dean came bashfully over. An hour later, in the drunkenness and chichiness of the party ('It's in honor of the end of the summer, of course'), he was kneeling on the floor with his chin on her belly and telling her and promising her everything and sweating. She was a big, sexy brunette—as García said, 'Something straight out of Degas,' and generally like a beautiful Parisian coquette. In a matter of days they were dickering with Camille in San Francisco by long-distance telephone for the necessary divorce papers so they could get married. Not only that, but a few months later Camille gave birth to Dean's second baby, the result of a few nights' rapport early in the year. And another matter of months and Inez had a baby. With one illegitimate child in the West somewhere, Dean then had four little ones and not a cent, and was all troubles and ecstasy and speed as ever. So we didn't go to Italy.

JACK KEROUAC

ZEN*

Ray Smith the narrator, riding the rails with the Diamond Sutra *in his pocket, looks for wisdom among his friends in California. He may not be a Bodhisattva, or great wise angel, yet; but he has avoided sex for a year because 'pretty girls make graves'. His friend Japhy Ryder, a Buddhist expert, regards sex as holy, and one night Ray shares Japhy's girlfriend Princess at a* yabyum *ceremony. Then, for illumination, Japhy, Ray, and a funny eccentric Morley, who forgets his sleeping bag, go on a great climb in the freezing Sierra Nevada range. Ray learns to jump easily from boulder to boulder. 'Like Zen. Don't think. Just dance along,' advises Japhy, who has the mild, generous quality of a follower of Zen and quotes the Chinese sage, Han Shan— though Japhy honours many forms of Buddhism, just as Ray later finds a parallel wisdom in the Bible's St Paul. Composing haikus, the friends without wine (but with plenty of chocolate pudding) see America's beauty as sublime. But Japhy, as a Dharma Bum, is too ashamed of his looks to want to enter a 'fancy restaurant' after the mountain descent. In this episode just after the climb, Princess arrives for some loving. Then Japhy the Buddhist, with a big, goodnatured poet named Coughlin, as well as Alvah Goldbook, the poet of 'Wail', and Ray all have a 'mad party' in a Berkeley cottage. Ray Smith is based on Kerouac himself, Japhy Ryder on Gary Snyder, and Alvah Goldbook on Allen Ginsberg.*

When I got up the next day I couldn't help smiling thinking of Japhy standing huddled in the night outside the fancy restaurant wondering if we would be let in or not. It was the first time I'd ever seen him afraid of anything. I planned to tell him about such things, that night, when he'd be coming over. But that night everything happened. First, Alvah left

*From *The Dharma Bums*.

88

and went out for a few hours and I was alone reading when suddenly I heard a bike in the yard and I looked and it was Princess.

'Where's everybody?' says she.

'How long can you stay?'

'I've got to go right away, unless I call my mother.'

'Let's call.'

'Okay.'

We went down to the corner gas station pay phone, and she said she'd be home in two hours, and as we walked back along the sidewalk I put my arm around her waist but way around with my fingers digging into her belly and she said '*Oooh*, I can't stand that!' and almost fell down on the sidewalk and bit my shirt just as an old woman was coming our way ogling us angrily and after she passed us we clinched in a big mad passionate kiss under the trees of evening. We rushed to the cottage where she spent an hour literally spinning in my arms and Alvah walked in right in the middle of our final ministrations of the Bodhisattva. We took our usual bath together. It was great sitting in the hot tub chatting and soaping each other's backs. Poor Princess, she meant every word she said. I really felt good about her, and compassionate, and even warned her: 'Now don't go wild and get into orgies with fifteen guys on a mountaintop.'

Japhy came after she left, and then Coughlin came and suddenly (we had wine) a mad party began in the cottage. It started off with Coughlin and me, drunk now, walking arm in arm down the main drag of town carrying huge, almost impossibly huge flowers of some kind we'd found in a garden, and a new jug of wine, shouting haikus and hoos and satoris at everybody we saw in the street and everybody was smiling at us. 'Walked five miles carrying huge flower,' yelled Coughlin, and I liked him now, he was deceptively scholarly looking or fatty-boomboom looking but he was a real man. We went to visit some professor of the English Department at U. of Cal. we knew and Coughlin left his shoes on the lawn and danced right into the astonished professor's house, in fact frightened him somewhat, though Coughlin was a fairly well known poet by now. Then barefooted with our huge flowers and jugs we went back to the cottage it was now about ten. I had just gotten some money in the mail that day, a fellowship of three hundred bucks, so I said to Japhy 'Well I've learned everything now, I'm ready. How about driving me to Oakland tomorrow and helping me buy all my rucksack and gear and stuff so I can take off for the desert?'

'Good, I'll get Morley's car and be over to get you first thing in the morning, but right now how about some of that wine?' I turned on the little red bandana dimbulb and we poured wine and all sat around talking. It was a great night of talk. First Japhy started telling his later life story, like when he was a merchant seaman in New York port and went around with a dagger on his hip, 1948, which surprised Alvah and me, and then about the girl he was in love with who lived in California: 'I had a hardon for her three thousand miles long, goodness!'

Then Coughlin said 'Tell 'em about Great Plum, Japh.'

Instantly Japhy said 'Great Plum Zen Master was asked what the great meaning of Buddhism was, and he said rush flowers, willow catkins, bamboo needles, linen thread, in other words hang on boy, the ecstasy's general, 's what he means, ecstasy of the mind, the world is nothing but mind and what is the mind? The mind is nothing but the world, goddammit. Then Horse Ancestor said "This mind is Buddha." He also said "No mind is Buddha." Then finally talking about Great Plum his boy, "The plum is ripe." '

'Well that's pretty interesting,' said Alvah, 'but Où sont les neiges d'antan?'

'Well I sort of agree with you because the trouble is these people saw the flowers like they were in a dream but dammit-all the world is *real* Smith and Goldbook and everybody carries on like it was a dream, shit, like they were themselves dreams or dots. Pain or love or danger makes you real again, ain't that right Ray like when you were scared on that ledge?'

'Everything was real, okay.'

'That's why frontiersmen are always heroes and were always my real heroes and will always be. They're constantly on the alert in the realness which might as well be real as unreal, what difference does it make, Diamond Sutra says "Make no formed conceptions about the realness of existence nor about the unrealness of existence," or words like that. Handcuffs will get soft and billy clubs will topple over, let's go on being free anyhow.'

'The President of the United States suddenly grows cross-eyed and floats away!' I yell.

'And anchovies will turn to dust!' yells Coughlin.

'The Golden Gate is creaking with sunset rust,' says Alvah.

'And anchovies will turn to dust,' insists Coughlin.

'Give me another slug of that jug. How! Ho! Hoo!' Japhy leaping up: 'I've been reading Whitman, know what he says, *Cheer up slaves, and horrify foreign despots*, he means that's the attitude for the Bard, the Zen Lunacy bard of old desert paths, see the whole thing is a world full of rucksack wanderers, Dharma Bums refusing to subscribe to the general demand that they consume production and therefore have to work for the privilege of consuming, all that crap they didn't really want anyway such as refrigerators, TV sets, cars, at least new fancy cars, certain hair oils and deodorants and general junk you finally always see a week later in the garbage anyway, all of them imprisoned in a system of work, produce, consume, work, produce, consume, I see a vision of a great rucksack revolution thousands or even millions of young Americans wandering around with rucksacks, going up to mountains to pray, making children laugh and old men glad, making young girls happy and old girls happier, all of 'em Zen Lunatics who go about writing poems that happen to appear in their heads for no reason and also by being kind and also by strange unexpected acts keep giving visions of eternal freedom to everybody and to all living creatures, that's what I like about you Goldbook and Smith, you two guys from the East Coast which I thought was dead.'

'We thought the *West* Coast was dead!'

'You've really brought a fresh wind around here. Why, do you realize the Jurassic pure granite of Sierra Nevada with the straggling high conifers of the last ice age and lakes we just saw is one of the greatest expressions on this earth, just think how truly great and wise America will be, with all this energy and exuberance and space focused into the Dharma.'

'Oh'—Alvah—'balls on that old tired Dharma.'

'Ho! What we need is a floating zendo, where an old Bodhisattva can wander from place to place and always be sure to find a spot to sleep in among friends and cook up mush.'

' "The boys was glad, and rested up for more, and Jack cooked mush, in honor of the door," ' I recited.

'What's that?'

'That's a poem I wrote. "The boys was sittin in a grove of trees, listenin to Buddy explain the keys. Boys, sez he, the Dharma is a door . . . Let's see . . . Boys, I say the keys, cause there's lotsa keys, but only one door, one hive for the bees. So listen to me, and I'll try to tell all, as I heard it long ago, in the Pure Land Hall. For you good boys, with winesoaked teeth, that can't understand these words on a heath, I'll make it simpler, like a bottle of wine, and a good woodfire, under stars divine. Now listen to me, and when you have learned the Dharma of the Buddhas of old and yearned, to sit down with the truth, under a lonesome tree, in Yuma Arizony, or anywhere you be, don't thank me for tellin, what was told me, this is the wheel I'm a-turnin, this is the reason I be: Mind is the Maker, for no reason at all, for all this creation, created to fall." '

'Ah but that's too pessimistic and like dream gucky,' says Alvah, 'though the rhyme is pure like Melville.'

'We'll have a floatin zendo for Buddy's winesoaked boys to come and lay up in and learn to drink tea like Ray did, learn to meditate like you should Alvah, and I'll be a head monk of a zendo with a big jar full of crickets.'

'Crickets?'

'Yessir, that's what, a series of monasteries for fellows to go and monastate and meditate in, we can have groups of shacks up in the Sierras or the High Cascades or even Ray says down in Mexico and have big wild gangs of pure holy men getting together to drink and talk and pray, think of the waves of salvation can flow out of nights like that, and finally have women, too, wives, small huts with religious families, like the old days of the Puritans. Who's to say the cops of America and the Republicans and Democrats are gonna tell everybody what to do?'

'What's the crickets?'

'Big jar full of crickets, give me another drink Coughlin, about one tenth of an inch long with huge white antennae and hatch 'em myself, little sentient beings in a bottle that sing real good when they grow up. I wanta swim in rivers and drink goatmilk and talk with priests and just read Chinese books and amble around the valleys talking to farmers and their children. We've got to have mind-collecting weeks in our zendos where your mind tries to fly off like a Tinker Toy and like a good soldier you put it back together with your eyes closed except of course the whole thing is wrong. D'y'hear my latest poem Goldbook?'

'No what?'

'Mother of children, sister, daughter of sick old man, virgin your blouse is torn, hungry and barelegged, I'm hungry too, take these poems.'

'Fine, fine.'

'I wanta bicycle in hot afternoon heat, wear Pakistan leather sandals, shout in high voice at Zen monk buddies standing in thin hemp summer robes and stubble heads, wanta live in golden pavilion temples, drink beer, say goodbye, go Yokahama big buzz Asia port full of vassals and vessels, hope, work around, come back, go, go to Japan, come back to U.S.A., read Hakuin, grit my teeth and discipline myself all the time while getting nowhere and thereby learn . . . learn that my body and everything gets tired and ill and droopy and so find out all about Hakuyu.'

'Who's Hakuyu?'

'His name meant White Obscurity, his name meant he who lived in the hills back of Northern-White-Water where I'm gonna go hiking, by God, it must be full of steep piney gorges and bamboo valleys and little cliffs.'

'I'll go with you!' (me).

'I wanta read about Hakuin, who went to see this old man who lived in a cave, slept with deer and ate chestnuts and the old man told him to quit meditating and quit thinking about koans, as Ray says, and instead learn how to go to sleep and wake up, said, when you go to sleep you should put your legs together and take deep breaths and then concentrate your mind on a spot one and a half inches below your navel until you feel it get like a ball of power and then start breathing from your heels clear up and concentrate saying to yourself that that center just here is Amida's Pure Land, the center of the mind, and when you wake up you should start by consciously breathing and stretching a little and thinking the same thoughts, see, the rest of the time.'

'That's what I like, see,' says Alvah, 'these actual signposts to something. What else?'

'The rest of the time he said don't bother about thinkin about nothin, just eat well, not too much, and sleep good, and old Hakuyu said he was three hundred friggin years old just then and figured he was good for five hundred more, by Gawd which makes me think he must still be up there if he's anybody at all.'

'Or the sheepherder kicked his dog!' puts in Coughlin.

'I bet I can find that cave in Japan.'

'You can't live in this world but there's nowhere else to go,' laughs Coughlin.

'What's that mean?' I ask.

'It means the chair I sit in is a lion throne and the lion is walking, he roars.'

'What's he say?'

'Says, Rahula! Rahula! Face of Glory! Universe chawed and swallowed!'

'Ah balls!' I yell.

'I'm goin to Marin County in a few weeks,' said Japhy, 'go walk a hunnerd times around Tamalpais and help purify the atmosphere and accustom the local spirits to the sound of sutra. What you think, Alvah?'

'I think it's all lovely hallucination but I love it sorta.'

'Alvah, trouble with you is you don't do plenty night zazen

especially when it's cold out, that's best, besides you should get married and have half breed babies, manuscripts, homespun blankets and mother's milk on your happy ragged mat floor like this one. Get yourself a hut house not too far from town, live cheap, go ball in the bars once in a while, write and rumble in the hills and learn how to saw boards and talk to grandmas you damn fool, carry loads of wood for them, clap your hands at shrines, get supernatural favors, take flower-arrangement lessons and grow chrysanthemums by the door, and get married for krissakes, get a friendly smart sensitive human-being gal who don't give a shit for martinis every night and all that dumb white machinery in the kitchen.'

'Oh,' says Alvah sitting up glad, 'and what else?'

'Think of barn swallows and nighthawks filling the fields. Do you know, say Ray, since yesterday I translated another stanza of Han Shan, lissen, "Cold Mountain is a house, without beams or walls, the six doors left and right are open, the hall is the blue sky, the rooms are vacant and empty, the east wall strikes the west wall, at the center not one thing. Borrowers don't trouble me, in the cold I build a little fire, when I'm hungry I boil up some greens, I've got no use for the kulak with his big barn and pasture . . . he just sets up a prison for himself, once in, he can't get out, think it over, it might happen to you." '

Then Japhy picked up his guitar and got going on songs; finally I took the guitar and made up a song as I went along plucking on the strings any old way, actually drumming on them with my fingertips, drum drum drum, and sang the song of the Midnight Ghost freight train. 'That's about the midnight ghost in California but you know what it made me think of Smith? Hot, very hot, bamboo growing up to forty feet out thar and whipping around in the breeze and hot and a bunch of monks are making a racket on their flutes somewhere and when they recite sutras with a steady Kwakiutl dance drumbeat and riffs on the bells and sticks it's something to hear like a big prehistoric coyote chanting. . . . Things tucked away in all you mad guys like that go back to the days when men married bears and talked to the buffalo by Gawd. Give me another drink. Keep your socks darned, boys, and your boots greased.'

But as though that wasn't enough Coughlin says quite calmly crosslegged 'Sharpen your pencils, straighten your ties, shine your shoes and button your flies, brush your teeth, comb your hair, sweep the floor, eat blueberry pies, open your eyes . . .'

'Eat blueberry spies is good,' says Alvah fingering his lip seriously.

'Remembering all the while that I have tried very hard, but the rhododendron tree is only half enlightened, and ants and bees are communists and trolley cars are bored.'

'And little Japanese boys in the F train sing Inky Dinky Parly Voo!' I yell.

'And the mountains live in total ignorance so I don't give up, take off your shoes and put 'em in your pocket. Now I've answered all your questions, too bad, give me a drink, mauvais sujet.'

'Don't step on the ballsucker!' I yell drunk.

'Try to do it without stepping on the aardvark,' says Coughlin. 'Don't be a sucker all you life, dummy up, ya dope. Do you see what I mean? My lion is fed, I sleep at his side.'

'Oh,' says Alvah, 'I wish I could take all this down.' And I was amazed, pretty amazed, by the fast wonderful yak yak yak darts in my sleeping brain. We all got dizzy and drunk. It was a mad night. It ended up with Coughlin and me wrestling and making holes in the wall and almost knocking the little cottage down: Alvah was pretty mad the next day. During the wrestling match I practically broke poor Coughlin's leg; myself, I got a bad splinter of wood stuck an inch up into my skin and it didn't come out till almost a year later. Meanwhile, at some point, Morley appeared in the doorway like a ghost carrying two quarts of yogurt and wanting to know if we wanted some. Japhy left at about two a.m. saying he'd come back and get me in the morning for our big day outfitting me with full pack. Everything was fine with the Zen Lunatics, the nut wagon was too far away to hear us. But there was a wisdom in it all, as you'll see if you take a walk some night on a suburban street and pass house after house on both sides of the street each with the lamplight of the living room, shining golden, and inside the little blue square of the television, each living family riveting its attention on probably one show; nobody talking; silence in the yards; dogs barking at you because you pass on human feet instead of on wheels. You'll see what I mean, when it begins to appear like everybody in the world is soon going to be thinking the same way and the Zen Lunatics have long joined dust, laughter on their dust lips. Only one thing I'll say for the people watching television, the millions and millions of the One Eye: they're not hurting anyone while they're sitting in front of that Eye. But neither was Japhy. . . . I see him in future years stalking along with full rucksack, in suburban streets, passing the blue television windows of homes, alone, his thoughts the only thoughts not electrified to the Master Switch. As for me, maybe the answer was in my little Buddy poem that kept on: ' "Who played this cruel joke, on bloke after bloke, packing like a rat, across the desert flat?" asked Montana Slim, gesturing to him, the buddy of the men, in this lion's den. "Was it God got mad, like the Indian cad, who was only a giver, crooked like the river? Gave you a garden, let it all harden, then comes the flood, and the loss of your blood? Pray tell us, good buddy, and don't make it muddy, who played this trick, on Harry and Dick, and why is so mean, this Eternal Scene, just what's the point, of this whole joint?" ' I thought maybe I could find out at last from these Dharma Bums.

WILLIAM BURROUGHS

MY FIRST DAYS ON JUNK*

My first experience with junk was during the War, about 1944 or 1945. I had made the acquaintance of a man named Norton who was working in a shipyard at the time. Norton, whose real name was Morelli or something like that, had been discharged from the peacetime Army for forging a pay check, and was classified 4-F for reasons of bad character. He looked like George Raft, but was taller. Norton was trying to improve his English and achieve a smooth, affable manner. Affability, however, did not come natural to him. In repose, his expression was sullen and mean, and you knew he always had that mean look when you turned your back.

Norton was a hard-working thief and he did not feel right unless he stole something every day from the shipyard where he worked. A tool, some canned goods, a pair of overalls, anything at all. One day he called me up and said he had stolen a Tommy gun. Could I find someone to buy it? I said, 'Maybe. Bring it over.'

The housing shortage was getting under way. I paid fifteen dollars a week for a dirty apartment that opened on to a companionway and never got any sunlight. The wallpaper was flaking off because the radiator leaked steam when there was any steam in it to leak. I had the windows sealed shut with a caulking of newspapers against the cold. The place was full of roaches and occasionally I killed a bedbug.

I was sitting by the radiator, a little damp from the steam, when I heard Norton's knock. I opened the door, and there he was standing in the dark hall with a big parcel wrapped in brown paper under his arm. He smiled and said, 'Hello.'

I said, 'Come in, Norton, and take off your coat.'

He unwrapped the Tommy gun and we assembled it and snapped the firing pin. I said I would find someone to buy it.

*From 'William Lee': *Junkie*.

Norton said, 'Oh, here's something else I picked up.'

It was a flat yellow box with five one-half grain syrettes of morphine tartrate.

'This is just a sample,' he said, indicating the morphine. 'I've got fifteen of these boxes at home and I can get more if you get rid of these.'

I said, 'I'll see what I can do.'

At that time I had never used any junk and it did not occur to me to try it. I began looking for someone to buy the two items and that is how I ran into Roy and Herman.

I knew a young hoodlum from upstate New York who was working as a short-order cook in Jarrow's, 'cooling off,' as he explained. I called him and said I had something to get rid of, and made an appointment to meet him in the Angle Bar on Eighth Avenue near 42nd Street.

This bar was a meeting place for 42nd Street hustlers, a peculiar breed of four-flushing, would-be criminals. They are always looking for a 'setup man,' someone to plan jobs and tell them exactly what to do. Since no 'setup man' would have anything to do with people so obviously inept, unlucky, and unsuccessful, they go on looking, fabricating preposterous lies about their big scores, cooling off as dishwashers, soda jerks, waiters, occasionally rolling a drunk or a timid queer, looking, always looking, for the 'setup man' with a big job who will say, 'I've been watching you. You're the man I need for this setup. Now listen . . .'

Jack—through whom I met Roy and Herman—was not one of these lost sheep looking for the shepherd with a diamond ring and a gun in the shoulder holster and the hard, confident voice with overtones of connections, fixes, setups that would make a stickup sound easy and sure of success. Jack was very successful from time to time and would turn up in new clothes and even new cars. He was also an inveterate liar who seemed to lie more for himself than for any visible audience. He had a clean-cut, healthy country face, but there was something curiously diseased about him. He was subject to sudden fluctuations in weight, like a diabetic or a sufferer from liver trouble.

These changes in weight were often accompanied by an uncontrollable fit of restlessness, so that he would disappear for some days.

The effect was uncanny. You would see him one time a fresh-faced kid. A week or so later he would turn up so thin, sallow and old-looking, you would have to look twice to recognize him. His face was lined with suffering in which his eyes did not participate. It was a suffering of his cells alone. He himself—the conscious ego that looked out of the glazed, alert-calm hoodlum eyes—would have nothing to do with this suffering of his rejected other self, a suffering of the nervous system, of flesh and viscera and cells.

He slid into the booth where I was sitting and ordered a shot of whisky. He tossed it off, put the glass down and looked at me with his head tilted a little to one side and back.

'What's this guy got?' he said.

'A Tommy gun and about thirty-five grains of morphine.'

'The morphine I can get rid of right away, but the Tommy gun may take a little time.'

Two detectives walked in and leaned on the bar talking to the bartender. Jack jerked his head in their direction. 'The law. Let's take a walk.'

I followed him out of the bar. He walked through the door sliding sideways. 'I'm taking you to someone who will want the morphine,' he said. 'You want to forget this address.'

We went down to the bottom level of the Independent Subway. Jack's voice, talking to his invisible audience, went on and on. He had a knack of throwing his voice directly into your consciousness. No external noise drowned him out. 'Give me a thirty-eight every time. Just flick back the hammer and let her go. I'll drop anyone at five hundred feet. Don't care what you say. My brother has two 30-caliber machine guns stashed in Iowa.'

We got off the subway and began to walk on snow-covered sidewalks between tenements.

'The guy owed me for a long time, see? I knew he had it but he wouldn't pay, so I waited for him when he finished work. I had a roll of nickels. No one can hang anything on you for carrying U.S. currency. Told me he was broke. I cracked his jaw and took my money off him. Two of his friends standing there, but they kept out of it. I'd've switched a blade on them.'

We were walking up tenement stairs. The stairs were made of worn black metal. We stopped in front of a narrow, metal-covered door, and Jack gave an elaborate knock inclining his head to the floor like a safecracker. The door was opened by a large, flabby, middle-aged queer, with tattooing on his forearms and even on the backs of his hands.

'This is Joey,' Jack said, and Joey said, 'Hello there.'

Jack pulled a five-dollar bill from his pocket and gave it to Joey. 'Get us a quart of Schenley's, will you, Joey?'

Joey put on an overcoat and went out.

In many tenement apartments the front door opens directly into the kitchen. This was such an apartment and we were in the kitchen.

After Joey went out I noticed another man who was standing there looking at me. Waves of hostility and suspicion flowed out from his large brown eyes like some sort of television broadcast. The effect was almost like a physical impact. The man was small and very thin, his neck loose in the collar of his shirt. His complexion faded from brown to a mottled yellow, and pancake make-up had been heavily applied in an attempt to conceal a skin eruption. His mouth was drawn down at the corners in a grimace of petulant annoyance.

'Who's this?' he said. His name, I learned later, was Herman.

'Friend of mine. He's got some morphine he wants to get rid of.'

Herman shrugged and turned out his hands. 'I don't think I want to bother, really.'

'Okay,' Jack said, 'we'll sell it to someone else. Come on, Bill.'

We went into the front room. There was a small radio, a china Buddha with a votive candle in front of it, pieces of bric-a-brac. A man was lying on a studio couch. He sat up as we entered the room and smiled pleasantly showing discolored, brownish teeth. It was a Southern voice with the accent of east Texas.

Jack said, 'Roy, this is a friend of mine. He has some morphine he wants to sell.'

The man sat up straighter and swung his legs off the couch. His jaw fell slackly, giving his face a vacant look. The skin of his face was smooth and brown. The cheekbones were high and he looked Oriental. His ears stuck out at right angles from his asymmetrical skull. The eyes were brown and they had a peculiar brilliance, as though points of light were shining behind them. The light in the room glinted on the points of light in his eyes like an opal.

'How much do you have?' he asked me.

'Seventy-five one-half grain syrettes.'

'The regular price is two dollars a grain,' he said, 'but syrettes go for a little less. People want tablets. Those syrettes have too much water and you have to squeeze the stuff out and cook it down.' He paused and his face went blank. 'I could go about one-fifty a grain,' he said finally.

'I guess that will be okay,' I said.

He asked how we could make contact and I gave him my phone number.

Joey came back with the whisky and we all had a drink. Herman stuck his head in from the kitchen and said to Jack, 'Could I talk to you for a minute?'

I could hear them arguing about something. Then Jack came back and Herman stayed in the kitchen. We all had a few drinks and Jack began telling a story.

'My partner was going through the joint. The guy was sleeping, and I was standing over him with a three-foot length of pipe I found in the bathroom. The pipe had a faucet on the end of it, see? All of a sudden he comes up and jumps straight out of bed, running. I let him have it with the faucet end, and he goes on running right out into the other room, the blood spurting out of his head ten feet every time his heart beat.' He made a pumping motion with his hand. 'You could see the brain there and the blood coming out of it.' Jack began to laugh uncontrollably. 'My girl was waiting out in the car. She called me—ha-ha-ha!—she called me—ha-ha-ha!—a cold-blooded killer.'

He laughed until his face was purple.

A few nights after meeting Roy and Herman, I used one of the syrettes, which was my first experience with junk. A syrette is like a toothpaste tube with a needle on the end. You push a pin down through the needle; the pin punctures the seal; and the syrette is ready to shoot.

Morphine hits the backs of the legs first, then the back of the neck, a spreading wave of relaxation slackening the muscles away from the bones so that you seem to float without outlines like lying in warm salt water. As this relaxing wave spread through my tissues, I experienced a strong feeling of fear. I had the feeling that some horrible image was just beyond the field of vision, moving, as I turned my head, so that I never quite saw it. I felt nauseous; I lay down and closed my eyes. A series of pictures passed, like watching a movie: A huge, neon-lighted cocktail bar that got larger and larger until streets, traffic, and street repairs were included in it; a waitress carrying a skull on a tray; stars in the clear sky. The physical impact of the fear of death; the shutting off of breath; the stopping of blood.

I dozed off and woke up with a start of fear. Next morning I vomited and felt sick until noon.

Roy called that night.

'About what we were discussing the other night,' he said. 'I could go about four dollars per box and take five boxes now. Are you busy? I'll come over to your place. We'll come to some kind of agreement.'

A few minutes later he knocked at the door. He had on a Glen plaid suit and a dark, coffee-colored shirt. We said hello. He looked around blankly and said, 'If you don't mind, I'll take one of those now.'

I opened the box. He took out a syrette and injected it into his leg. He pulled up his pants briskly and took out twenty dollars. I put five boxes on the kitchen table.

'I think I'll take them out of the boxes,' he said. 'Too bulky.'

He began putting the syrettes in his coat pockets. 'I don't think they'll perforate this way,' he said. 'Listen, I'll call you again in a day or so after I get rid of these and have some more money.' He was adjusting his hat over his asymmetrical skull. 'I'll see you.'

Next day he was back. He shot another syrette and pulled out forty dollars. I laid out ten boxes and kept two.

'These are for me,' I said.

He looked at me, surprised. 'You use it?'

'Now and then.'

'It's bad stuff,' he said, shaking his head. 'The worst thing that can happen to a man. We all think we can control it at first. Sometimes we don't want to control it.' He laughed. 'I'll take all you can get at this price.'

Next day he was back. He asked if I didn't want to change my mind about selling the two boxes. I said no. He bought two syrettes for a dollar each, shot them both, and left. He said he had signed on for a two-month trip.

During the next month I used up the eight syrettes I had not sold. The fear I had experienced after using the first syrette was not noticeable after the third; but still, from time to time, after taking a shot I would wake up with a start of fear. After six weeks or so I gave Roy a ring, not expecting him to be back from his trip, but then I heard his voice on the phone.

I said, 'Say, do you have any to sell? Of the material I sold you before?'

There was a pause.

'Ye-es,' he said, 'I can let you have six, but the price will have to be three dollars per. You understand I don't have many.'

'Okay,' I said. 'You know the way. Bring it on over.'

It was twelve one-half grain tablets in a thin glass tube. I paid him eighteen dollars and he apologized again for the retail rate.

Next day he bought two grains back.

'It's mighty hard to get now at any price,' he said, looking for a vein in his leg. He finally hit a vein and shot the liquid in with an air bubble. 'If air bubbles could kill you, there wouldn't be a junkie alive.'

Later that day Roy pointed out to me a drugstore where they sold needles without any questions—very few drugstores will sell them without a prescription. He showed me how to make a collar out of paper to fit the needle to any eyedropper. An eyedropper is easier to use than a regular hypo, especially for giving yourself vein shots.

Several days later Roy sent me to see a doctor with a story about kidney stones, to hit him for a morphine prescription. The doctor's wife slammed the door in my face, but Roy finally got past her and made the doctor for a ten-grain script.

The doctor's office was in junk territory on 102nd, off Broadway. He was a doddering old man and could not resist the junkies who filled his office and were, in fact, his only patients. It seemed to give him a feeling of importance to look out and see an office full of people. I guess he had reached a point where he could change the appearance of things to suit his needs and when he looked out there he saw a distinguished and diversified clientele, probably well-dressed in 1910 style, instead of a bunch of ratty-looking junkies come to hit him for a morphine script.

Roy shipped out at two- or three-week intervals. His trips were Army Transport and generally short. When he was in town we generally split a few scripts. The old croaker on 102nd finally lost his mind altogether and no drugstore would fill his scripts, but Roy located an Italian doctor out in the Bronx who would write.

I was taking a shot from time to time, but I was a long way from having a habit. At this time I moved into an apartment on the Lower East Side. It was a tenement apartment with the front door opening into the kitchen.

I began dropping into the Angle Bar every night and saw quite a bit of Herman. I managed to overcome his original bad impression of me, and soon I was buying his drinks and meals, and he was hitting me for 'smash' (change) at regular intervals. Herman did not have a habit at this time. In fact, he seldom got a habit unless someone else paid for it. But he was always high on something—weed, benzedrine, or knocked out of his mind on 'goof balls.' He showed up at the Angle every night with a big slob called Whitey. There were four Whiteys in the Angle set, which made for confusion. This Whitey combined the sensitivity of a neurotic with a psychopath's readiness for violence. He was convinced that nobody liked him, a fact that seemed to cause him a great deal of worry.

One Tuesday night Roy and I were standing at the end of the Angle bar. Subway Mike was there, and Frankie Dolan. Dolan was an Irish boy with a cast in one eye. He specialized in crummy scores, beating up defenseless drunks, and holding out on his confederates. 'I got no honor,' he would say. 'I'm a rat.' And he would giggle.

Subway Mike had a large, pale face and long teeth. He looked like some specialized kind of underground animal that preys on the animals of the surface. He was a skillful lush-worker, but he had no front. Any cop would do a double-take at the sight of him, and he was well known to the subway squad. So Mike spent at least half of his time on the Island doing 'five-twenty-nine' for jostling.

This night Herman was knocked out on 'nembies' and his head kept falling down onto the bar. Whitey was stomping up and down the length of the bar trying to promote some free drinks. The boys at the bar sat rigid and tense, clutching their drinks, quickly pocketing their change. I heard Whitey say to the bartender, 'Keep this for me, will you?' and he passed his large clasp knife across the bar. The boys sat there silent and gloomy under the fluorescent lights. They were all afraid of Whitey, all except Roy. Roy sipped his beer grimly. His eyes shone with their peculiar phosphorescence. His long asymmetrical body was draped against the bar. He didn't look at Whitey, but at the opposite wall where the booths were located. Once he said to me, 'He's no more drunk than I am. He's just thirsty.'

Whitey was standing in the middle of the bar, his fists doubled up, tears streaming down his face. 'I'm no good,' he said. 'I'm no good. Can't anyone understand I don't know what I'm doing?'

The boys tried to get as far away from him as possible without attracting his attention.

Subway Slim, Mike's occasional partner, came in and ordered a beer. He was tall and bony, and his ugly face had a curiously inanimate look, as if made out of wood. Whitey slapped him on the back and I heard Slim say, 'For Christ's sake, Whitey.' There was more interchange I didn't hear. Somewhere along the line Whitey must have got his knife back from the bartender. He got behind Slim and suddenly pushed his hand against Slim's back. Slim fell forward against the bar, groaning. I saw Whitey walk to the front of the bar and look around. He closed his knife and slipped it into his pocket.

Roy said, 'Let's go.'

Whitey had disappeared and the bar was empty except for Mike who was holding Slim up on one side. Frankie Dolan was on the other.

I heard next day from Frankie that Slim was okay. 'The croaker at the hospital said the knife just missed a kidney.'

Roy said, 'The big slob. I can see a real muscle man, but a guy like that going around picking up dimes and quarters off the bar. I was ready for him. I was going to kick him in the belly first, then get one of those quart beer bottles from the case on the floor and break it over his sconce. With a big villain like that you've got to use strategy.'

We were all barred from the Angle, which shortly afterwards changed its name to the Kent Grill.

One night I went to the Henry Street address to look up Jack. A tall, red-haired girl met me at the door.

'I'm Mary,' she said. 'Come in.'

It seemed that Jack was in Washington on business.

'Come on into the front room,' she said, pushing aside a red corduroy curtain. 'I talk to landlords and bill collectors in the kitchen. We *live* in here.'

I looked around. The bric-a-brac had gone. The place looked like a chop suey joint. There were black and red lacquered tables scattered around, black curtains covered the window. A colored wheel had been painted on the ceiling with little squares and triangles of different colors giving a mosaic effect.

'Jack did that,' Mary said, pointing to the wheel. 'You should have seen him. He stretched a board between two ladders and lay down on it. Paint kept dripping into his face. He gets a kick out of doing things like that. We get some frantic kicks out of that wheel when we're high. We lay on our backs and dig the wheel and pretty soon it begins to spin. The longer you watch it, the faster it spins.'

This wheel had the nightmarish vulgarity of Aztec mosaics, the bloody, vulgar nightmare, the heart throbbing in the morning sun, the garish pinks and blues of souvenir ashtrays, postcards and calendars. The walls were painted black and there was a Chinese character in red lacquer on one wall.

'We don't know what it means,' she said.

'Shirts thirty-one cents,' I suggested.

She turned on me her blank, cold smile. She began talking about Jack. 'I'm queer for Jack,' she said. 'He works at being a thief just like any job. Used to come home nights and hand me his gun. "Stash that!" He likes to work around the house, painting and making furniture.'

As she talked she moved around the room, throwing herself from one chair to another, crossing and uncrossing her legs, adjusting her slip, so as to give me a view of her anatomy in installments.

She went on to tell me how her days were numbered by a rare disease. 'Only twenty-six cases on record. In a few years I won't be able to get around at all. You see, my system can't absorb calcium and the bones are slowly dissolving. My legs will have to be amputated eventually, then the arms.'

There was something boneless about her, like a deep sea creature. Her eyes were cold fish-eyes that looked at you through a viscous medium she carried about with her. I could see those eyes in a shapeless, protoplasmic mass undulating over the dark sea floor.

'Benzedrine is a good kick,' she said. 'Three strips of the paper or about ten tablets. Or take two strips of benny and two goof balls. They get down there and have a fight. It's a good drive.'

Three young hoodlums from Brooklyn drifted in, wooden-faced, hands-in-pockets, stylized as a ballet. They were looking for Jack. He had given them a short count in some deal. At least, that was the general idea. They conveyed their meaning less by words than by significant jerks of the head and by stalking around the apartment and leaning against the walls. At length, one of them walked to the door and jerked his head. They filed out.

'Would you like to get high?' Mary asked. 'There may be a roach around here somewhere.' She began rummaging around in drawers and ashtrays. 'No, I guess not. Why don't we go uptown? I know several good connections we can probably catch about now.'

A young man lurched in with some object wrapped in brown paper under one arm. 'Ditch this on your way out,' he said, putting it down on the table. He staggered into the bedroom on the other side of the kitchen. When we got outside I let the wrapping paper fall loose revealing the coin box of a pay toilet crudely jimmied open.

In Times Square we got into a taxi and began cruising up and down the side streets, Mary giving directions. Every now and then she would yell 'Stop!' and jump out, her red hair streaming, and I would see her overhaul some character and start talking. 'The connection was here about ten minutes ago. This character's holding, but he won't turn loose of any.' Later: 'The regular connection is gone for the night. He lives in the Bronx. But just stop here for a minute. I may find someone in Rich's.' Finally: 'No one seems to be anywhere. It's a bit late to score. Let's buy some benny tubes and go over to Denny's. They have some gone numbers on the box. We can order coffee and get high on benny.'

Denny's was a spot near 52nd and Sixth where musicians came for fried chicken and coffee after one p.m. We sat down in a booth and ordered coffee. Mary cracked a benzedrine tube expertly, extracting the folded paper, and handed me three strips. 'Roll it up into a pill and wash it down with coffee.'

The paper gave off a sickening odor of menthol. Several people sitting nearby sniffed and smiled. I nearly gagged on the wad of paper, but finally got it down. Mary selected some gone numbers and beat on the table with the expression of a masturbating idiot.

I began talking very fast. My mouth was dry and my spit came out in round white balls—spitting cotton, it's called. We were walking around Times Square. Mary wanted to locate someone with a 'piccolo' (victrola). I was full of expansive, benevolent feelings, and suddenly wanted to call on people I hadn't seen in months or even years, people I did not like and who did not like me. We made a number of unsuccessful attempts to locate the ideal piccolo-owning host. Somewhere along the line we picked up Peter and finally decided to go back to the Henry Street apartment where there was at least a radio.

Peter and Mary and I spent the next thirty hours in the apartment. From time to time we would make coffee and swallow more benzedrine. Mary was describing the techniques she used to get money from the 'Johns' who formed her principal source of revenue.

'Always build a John up. If he has any sort of body at all, say, "Oh, don't ever hurt me." A John is different from a sucker. When you're with a sucker you're on the alert all the time. You give him nothing. A sucker is just to be taken. But a John is different. You give him what he pays for. When you're with him you enjoy yourself and you want him to enjoy himself, too.

'If you want to really bring a man down, light a cigarette in the middle of intercourse. Of course, I really don't like men at all sexually. What I really dig is chicks. I get a kick out of taking a proud chick and breaking her spirit, making her see she is just an animal. A chick is never beautiful after she's been broken. Say, this is sort of a fireside kick,' she said, pointing to the radio which was the only light in the room. Her face contorted into an expression of monkey-like rage as she talked about men who accosted her on the street. 'Sonofabitch!' she snarled. 'They can tell when a woman isn't looking for a pickup. I used to cruise around with brass knuckles on under my gloves just waiting for one of those peasants to crack at me.'

*

One day Herman told me about a kilo of first-class New Orleans' weed I could pick up for seventy dollars. Pushing weed looks good on paper, like fur farming or raising frogs. At seventy-five cents a stick, seventy sticks to the ounce, it sounded like money. I was convinced, and bought the weed.

Herman and I formed a partnership to push the weed. He located a Lesbian named Marian who lived in the Village and said she was a poetess. We kept the weed in Marian's apartment, turned her on for all she could use, and gave her a 50 per cent commission on the sales. She knew a lot of teaheads. Another Lesbian moved in with her, and every time I went to Marian's apartment, there was this huge red-haired Lizzie watching me with her cold fish-eyes full of stupid hate.

One day, the red-haired Lizzie opened the door and stood there, her face dead white and puffy with nembutal sleep. She shoved the package of weed at me. 'Take this and get out,' she said. She looked at us through heavily lidded eyes. 'You bastards!'

I said, 'Tell Marian thanks for everything.'

She slammed the door. The noise evidently woke her up. She opened the door again and began screaming with hysterical rage. We could still hear her out on the street.

Herman contacted other teaheads. They all gave us static.

In practice, pushing weed is a headache. To begin with, weed is bulky. You need a full suitcase to realize any money. If the cops start kicking your door in, it's like being with a bale of alfalfa.

Teaheads are not like junkies. A junkie hands you the money, takes his junk and cuts. But teaheads don't do things that way. They expect the peddler to light them up and sit around talking for half an hour to sell two dollars' worth of weed. If you come right to the point, they say you are a 'bring down.' In fact, a peddler should not come right out and say he is a peddler. No, he just scores for a few good 'cats' and 'chicks' because he is viperish. Everyone knows that he himself is the connection, but it is bad form to say so. God knows why. To me, teaheads are unfathomable.

There are a lot of trade secrets in the tea business, and

teaheads guard these supposed secrets with imbecilic slyness. For example, tea must be cured, or it is green and rasps the throat. But ask a teahead how to cure weed and he will give you a sly, stupid look and come-on with some doubletalk. Perhaps weed does affect the brain with constant use, or maybe teaheads are naturally silly.

The tea I had was green so I put it in a double boiler and set the boiler in the oven until the tea got the greenish-brown look it should have. This is the secret of curing tea, or at least one way to do it.

Teaheads are gregarious, they are sensitive, and they are paranoiac. If you get to be known as a 'drag' or a 'bring down,' you can't do business with them. I soon found out I couldn't get along with these characters and I was glad to find someone to take the tea off my hands at cost. I decided right then I would never push any more tea.

JOHN CLELLON HOLMES

GO*

Performances, assortments, resumés: the weekend of the Fourth was made of these. Everyone's enthusiasm rose continually during the two days, as if they all cherished in their heart's privacy some extraordinary memory of the holiday, long since considered infantile but still capable of evoking for each the hot, lost forenoons in all their American hometowns.

Then, the box of fireworks had been carried out into the street to be set off in a lavish squander, which consumed everything before the day lengthened into green afternoons and parades, and forced them to be content thereafter with what hungry ecstasy could be gained from the detonations of others.

These buried memories rose in everyone's mind, and as though each was secretly intent on recapturing or reducing the recollection, the simplicities of noise and chatter invested them, and they became as babbling and foolish and imaginative as children.

There was something fortuitous in their gathering, without previous arrangement, on the fretful, rainy Friday night when they tore up to Verger's in the Cadillac. Hart dashed about, helping Kathryn into her raincoat; and then grasping Dinah about the shoulders gruffly and ogling her, he exclaimed: 'Lotsa weed tonight and crazy music! You dig that, woman?'

She laughed with an intimate twinkle in her large blue eyes, with a glance that assured him of her appreciation of his attention, but his words meant nothing to her; in fact, neither of them believed in words, and only used them to hint at

*One of the first 'Beat' novels, Go (1952) was also to some extent a *roman à clef*: David Stofsky is modelled on Allen Ginsberg, Gene Pasternak on Jack Kerouac, Paul Hobbes on Clellon Holmes himself, and Hart Kennedy on Neal Cassady (also depicted by Jack Kerouac as Dean Moriarty in *On The Road* and Cody Pomeray in *Big Sur*, among his other appearances).

some inexpressible thought. Then Dinah turned to Kathryn, establishing a secretive, womanly air as easily as she had just acknowledged Hart's masculine joy, and said:

'You fix up your hair like that all the time? It looks real cute on you. But, you know, I feel all funny in this ol' dress. It's all we brought along though. They kidnapped me out of Denver without giving me even a chance to pack anything!' Then they were off into the wet lights and snarlings of the midtown streets.

Verger's damp, bare rooms were permeated with his feeling of exclusion from possible celebrations that were going on elsewhere. He lay, sprawled weakly on one of his cots, among bookish refuse. The others with him, Ketcham and a brittle, arrogant girl called May who lived next door, could not raise him from his depression, and, as if to remind them of their continuing failures, he would cough raspingly every few minutes, hunching his thin body and then falling exhaustedly into the pillows again, and say no word.

The sudden influx of Hart, Dinah, Kathryn, Hobbes, Pasternak and Ed Schindel who, because of the excitement of the dash uptown, did not recognize his mood, brought him to his feet with a self conscious, hacking laugh to rustle among plates and tin cans in the kitchen for glasses.

The radio was turned on, angular shadows danced in the top corners near a chipped place in the ceiling through which the ribs of the building shone whitely; laughter echoed, then filled the crowding silence.

Kathryn sank down beside Ketcham, who said: 'Thank God, you've come! It was getting awful and I was just about to leave. She's been insulting him for an hour, and he wouldn't say a word. He's like a lovesick schoolboy with her. Yes, with May! . . . But you know, I called you two yesterday, thinking the three of us could have dinner, but I couldn't get you in.' His relief made him unusually warm.

Dinah stood, between kitchen and living room, eyeing not so much the furnitureless apartment with its creaking, worn floors and its dreary unpainted walls that were scarred with old holes in which decades of portraits, calendars, snapshots and saints' pictures had hung, but surveying with watchful, pleasant interest the first clusterings of the others. Hart, who somehow usurped the hostly functions wherever he went, was speaking excitedly to Verger at the encouragement of Pasternak, while Ed, who dwarfed the room, smiled with self-effacing benignity nearby.

Dinah, a slim, fresh, pale eighteen, was pliant and yet fragile, a self-possessed bluebell of a girl who gave those around her a certain intangible security by her presence. She had a comradely, direct gaze that was bestowed impersonally on all but Hart. She seemed a wise child, without confusions, utterly wrapped in the moment's developments but distrusting analysis of them, and aware only of the look and gait and mood of others. Her oval face glowed with a feeble girlish flush, and her wide eyes calculated upon life attentively.

Now she chatted with the affected May, who answered in a shrill voice:

'Oh, yes, I'm living next door with a girl friend, you know. I really don't mind the neighborhood because I think everyone should have their year of bohemianism—although, of course, my mother would be horrified if she knew I was living in Spanish Harlem. But I suppose all mothers are that way, don't you think?'

'We're looking for a place,' Dinah replied with an affable calm as though she had somehow evaded May's affectations. 'Do you happen to know of one? We're staying with David right now, down on York Avenue . . . David Stofsky. But we can't stay in his pad permanently. I've got a job in a Rexall's starting on Tuesday, so we'll have enough cash.'

Verger brought whiskey, which Dinah declined sweetly with this: 'Oh no, thanks, I never drink any more. Two years ago I was real lush and drinking a quart a day, but I don't pick up now. I even tried to kill myself once.' It was no confession, no effort to impress, but simply a friendly remark as she said it. Verger hovered near May for a moment, watching her with sad tenderness, blind to her foolish words and flighty gestures, a patient sorrowful adoration on his face which she ignored expertly.

At that moment, announcing themselves with a muffled rumbling through the halls, Agatson and a disconsolate crowd appeared, only half of them coated against the rain. The others were soaked and Agatson, in the tattered, shrunken pair of blue jeans and turtle neck sweater, looking as unshaven and fierce as a thirsty Portuguese fisherman, shouted: 'Is everyone drunk around here? Who are all these people? Who lives in this joint? . . . Ketcham, what are you doing *here* of all places? Bianca was asking about you just last night, yes, yes! I told her to shut up and stop being sincere! . . . Is anyone real drunk? . . . I just walked up the street on the car-tops, and hit only one convertible!'

He was with a Village crowd which, like so many others that night, had come together accidentally and set out restlessly wandering to find themselves in Verger's desolate neighborhood by the river. Now they straggled in and out of his rooms, poking suspiciously into everything, grabbing unguarded glasses and going at the liquor.

Verger was overwhelmed, and as nervous as he always was when Agatson was around, and sat on the floor amid the feet, drinking and coughing. Then, pushed into a corner by their comings and goings, he huddled with an old, rusty long-sword which leaned there like the emblem of some deflated ideal he was reluctant to finally bury. He stabbed at the floorboards with an ironical fervor, not caring how they cavorted among his precious books, but only peeping at May occasionally and, finding her intent upon the tousled and raucous Agatson, returned to his chipping with renewed introspection.

Time withdrew and their excitement flourished. Hart gathered Hobbes, Kathryn and Pasternak together and herding them into the bathroom with Dinah, extracted a stick of marijuana from his hip pocket.

'O.K.,' he exclaimed as though someone had ventured a question. 'We'll pick up in here, see. There isn't enough for anybody else so there's no use broadcasting it, is there? You dig what I mean? Just cut back in here once in a while and we'll light up real cozy, okay?'

He lit the cigarette, giggling and laughing and talking

between puffs, then held it to their mouths one after the other. Dinah closed her eyes ecstatically and sucked deeply three long times, holding her breath after each.

'Yes!' Hart broke out. 'Yes, yes! Again, baby! Go ahead, another one! That's right!'

Outside, May was being pulled about by Agatson, his eyes burning viciously, in a formless dance. The music came from the same all-night program of wild jazz that midnight unleashed to all the city's hidden, backstairs pads where feverish young people gathered over their intoxicants to listen and not to listen; or hipsters woke, like some mute and ancient dead, to have their first cigarette of the 'day.' The night hours vanished before this music's bizarre imagery, until it finally evaporated into news reports at dawn like a demon turning into a tree.

Across the room from where Hobbes sat on a cot drinking, Kathryn drifted into Pasternak, who was bobbing regularly to the music.

'My God, Pasternak, don't you ever get tired of this noise?'

'What do you mean? Listen, that guy's actually *laying* his horn! You don't listen to it!'

'How the hell can I help but listen to it!' and she laughed scornfully and had some of his drink. They lingered together awkwardly, unable to speak in any but crude, sparring words, yet perilously joined by an unwilling curiosity and awareness concerning each other.

But now Hart and Dinah had started to dance, she clinging about his neck lithely with both bare arms, her head averted into his shoulder. He gripped her hips with large hands and moved her to him and away as though he had tapped a world of grace and abandon inside her and could direct it at will. Their feet hardly moved, but the rest of their bodies weaved rhythmically; she, lidded, trance-like as though in a swoon of dreamy surrender; he, unyielding, compulsive and yet also precise as he pressed her against his chest tighter and tighter.

The room's attention pivoted to them: Ed and Verger watching complacently; Agatson as though it was a clever diversion; Kathryn and Pasternak with an intent, yet somehow dispassionate interest.

May, however, frowned with disgust, shaking her head, and muttered: 'Good God!' She searched the faces of the others for agreement, sure they would feel that the mysterious antagonism between the sexes, which she found exhilarating and necessary, should not be so willingly and simply dispensed with.

When it was over, and the others resumed their shuffling about in the weird light, Hobbes found Pasternak beside him, saying eagerly: 'Isn't Hart terrific? And he's like that all the time! He doesn't care about anything! He yells "go!" to everything, everything!'

'Sure, Gene, but the word for that is "come!" not "go!" Haha! . . . Come!'

If this was the wrong sort of answer, Pasternak gave no explanations, but lurched immediately away.

Time withdrew before the tide of saxophones that taxed the radio, now rising over the lunging drums in banshee screams which brought shouts from the dimmer corners, then skittering pell mell down some slope of melody as the rhythm broke on a wild, hard phrase. Trips to the bathroom and the weed, which never seemed to run out, made all sensation more fragmentary, bizarre, grotesque. People lay knotted together grimly, while others danced in stumbling gaiety, or fought their way to glasses. Talk capsuled into exclamations and laughter; the sense of having watchers around vanished from everyone's mind, and they wandered about, paired off, retired to corners, started conversations and abandoned them unfinished.

Hobbes hovered alone by a wall, dizzy from the drinking and the marijuana, and snagged in the senseless return of an old inferiority, cherishing a fond sadness as though he had perceived in all the chaos a deep vein of desperation which everyone else refused to notice. 'Out of what rage and loneliness do we come together?' he thought drunkenly, certain some obsure wisdom lurked in the question. 'Don't you ever ask yourselves why?' And he fancied, through his dizziness, that he was speaking aloud.

'What's wrong? Are you feeling all right?' a voice said in the din, piercing his monologue. 'Is anything wrong?' It was

Kathryn, face flushed with a half smile, half frown. 'You've been scowling for hours, and I'm drunk as all hell!'

'Oh, *you* know,' he replied thickly. 'The ridiculous questions. What about me! How do I fit into this! . . . Humph! You know.'

'Jesus Christ, why do you always have to get like that?'

'Well, go away then and have another drink. Go ahead. Where's the end of the night? That's all I was thinking. The whole long night! But go have a drink.'

'We can leave whenever you want, but I thought you were having a good time. It was your idea.' And she went away with irritation, before he could say that that was not what he had meant at all. So he sat there, knowing that the thoughts had risen in his head because he was dizzy and felt like vomiting, but not realizing that he had skillfully prevented both of them from recognizing this fact.

A commotion suddenly broke out near the windows. Verger, risen from the floor where he had been immobile most of the evening, stood, like a wheezing Golem, brandishing his sword wildly, and was methodically pouring the only remaining bottle of whiskey out the window into the rain. Agatson leapt up from the mattress where he had been thrusting with a disheveled May, and tried to rescue the bottle; but Verger, who endorsed temperance when he was drunk, let it go and there was a distant explosion of glass in the backyards below.

'Now why did you have to do that?' May was moaning thickly. ' . . . very childish when you get stinking that way . . .'

As if to fight away some Calvinist Satan of his imagination represented by the tottering figure of Agatson, Verger started swinging the sword crazily, eyes aflame and a strange laugh twisted on his lips. Somebody roared above the radio, laughter screeched in the darkness somewhere, like the mocking of sharp beaked, unblinking birds; and then, at a furious swing which Agatson made no effort to keep away from, the sword crashed through the window nearby, throwing Verger off his balance. As though a trap had been sprung, he thudded stiffly to the floor among the shattered glass, still weakly clutching his rusty weapon.

'O.B.! O.B.! O.B.!' Agatson chanted over his prone body, making a wild sign of the cross.

'A window's broken,' Kathryn yelled in the kitchen. 'Let's get the hell out of here before the cops come!'

And, as if this charade had brought something to an end, Hart gathered them all together around the sink and said: 'We're out of liquor and weed, see, but there's this friend of Ketcham's here that knows a connection up in Harlem, so we'll cut up there to this after-hours joint he knows!'

So they all slipped away, joined by Ketcham and his friend, Ben, a smiling fellow with a smell of benzedrine about him, who loped down the stairs with them, making vague jokes in a midwestern drawl. As they went through the halls, the indifference of the colorless doors and the emaciated cats they found on every landing, and of all physical things, to their very presence, drove them further into their hilarity.

As though they were the creations of that night, it drove them, drunk and sober, towards the dawn, through a jumble of dreary streets to still drearier precincts, conglomerate with derelict houses where no light showed, that were fronted by bent iron railings, crusted and awry. The steady drenching of the rain made this Acheron of tenements appear more miserably squalid, and the car careened onward, Hobbes muttering, each time Hart swerved around a torturous corner: 'Go! Go!'

They jerked to a halt just off One Hundred and Thirty-eighth Street and, leaping out, Ben leading the way, approached a darkened brownstone no different than its neighbors, where, gathering at the top of the stairs, they were greeted by a large, grave Negro, who smiled distantly as he held the door wider for them to enter, saying: 'Good evening, gentlemen. Step right inside, just through that door . . .'

Beyond a room of sofas and ash-stands which had once been the front parlor, was a high ceilinged, drab hall, its windows tacked over with dusty black velvet, a bar built on one side and a scattering of circular tables filling the other. The room was crowded with people, mostly Negroes; the single drinkers at the bar, the parties squeezed around the tables. In the heavy yellow glow from a dim, crystal chandelier—a light as flickering and unreal as if it had come from tapers—an opulent Negro woman was singing, accompanied by a grinning guitarist in a sports shirt, and by an intense pianist, whose cocked head seemed tuned in on some wild poetry within the music which his dark fingers, spidering along the keys, endeavored to draw from the prosaic upright.

Amiably, Ben collected four dollars, managing to edge into a space at the bar, and ordered four drinks, all they could afford. No one seemed to notice them; the faces lining the walls were hot, placid, distracted.

The singer, stamping her foot three times, led off into a fresh burst of song, raising her arms in graceful supplication. 'All of me-ee-ee . . . Why . . . not . . . take . . . all of me-ee-ee!' She started sliding between the tables, head thrown back, pausing at each with her hands expressively outstretched in appeal. The guitarist shuffled along behind her, muttering encouragements. Her dusky eyes leveled knowingly at each customer and, as though each saw there and heard in the music the memory they all must have attached to this rebellious and wistful American jazz which was somehow most expressive of the boiling, deaf cities and the long brown reaches of their country, at every table a dollar was pressed into her hand, and with a swing of generous breasts she would move on.

Hobbes, caught up in the living music, gravitated to the piano she left behind. At every fresh chorus, the ascetic Negro there released greater ringing chords, as though the increasing distance of the voice brought the inner melody closer to his poised ear. Hobbes, leaning toward him, was, through his giddiness, suddenly possessed by the illusion of emotional eloquence and started to chant softly, improvising broken phrases. The Negro glanced up for an instant, nodding abstractly, long gone, and with no resentment at the intrusion.

It was a room which day, and the things of the day, had not entered, perhaps for decades; and everyone there was aware of where they were, and of the illegality of it, and yet because of this and the sensual voice of the woman, still moving like some buxom priestess among them, they were caught up together.

121

Pasternak, against a wall where he and Kathryn stood close sharing a drink between them, exclaimed: 'But it's all the same! Everything's the same as everything else! Every *one!* . . . Baydo-baydo-boo-ba! Can you hear it? . . . But look, look at Hart go!'

The singer was moving across the open space toward the bar and Hart, his head bobbing up and down and his eyes narrowed, was shuffling to meet her, stooped over and clapping his hands like an euphoric savage who erupts into a magic rite at the moment of his seizure. She watched him coming toward her, with dark experienced eyes, and for an instant sang just for him, her shoulders swinging on the deep strums of the guitarist who tarried behind, watchful and yet also appreciative. Hart stopped before her, bobbing, ecstatic, and then, falling down on his knees, he cried: 'Y-e-s! Blow! Blow! . . . You know who you are!'; for this was his offering, all he could give. And, as if she accepted it in lieu of money, with a wave of her head, a bright wink at the crowd, and a great display of heaving bosom, she strutted on.

Dinah was smiling faintly, all this and much more being usual for her, allowing him to have it without a word as proof of her commitment to him at that moment. He could say nothing, but laughed hoarsely and took her about the shoulders. There was one more prolonged, incredible chorus, and with a last smile, the singer disappeared and the music was over. Having no more money and having come to some consummation, they all straggled out and into the car again.

Ben's connection had not showed; the sweet cologne fragrance of benzedrine about him and the discoloration of his lips suggested that there may have been no marijuana connection at all, but somehow that did not matter. Continuance was what concerned them, and where to go next. After a number of improbable ideas (places that would not be open, people who would not be up), they settled on a friend of Ben's who lived on One Hundred and Twenty-third Street and Amsterdam Avenue, who would 'surely have liquor.' Although at another moment this would have seemed unlikely to them all, now they believed it with bland innocence as though all discord in the universe had been resolved by their harmony, which, in any case, did not depend on such details.

They rode as in a sunken city whose life is frozen in watery silence, they alone capable of breath and words, and finally pulled up before another dead house on another bleak street. But as if a morning premonition had touched them, and all felt for the first time a slackening, they groped down a long corridor in a centerless throng. They reached the end of it and went down a treacherous stairway into a dismal backyard, empty of all but garbage cans collecting rain, up two more steps and then, like movie spies taking absurdly circuitous routes, through a window with a broken sash, to find themselves in a chilly, enameled kitchen where people were blankly sitting, drinking coffee. Sensing hostility and leaving the amenities to Ben, they dispersed into the dark echoing rooms beyond, which were filled with incongruous furniture (the rightful refuse of country attics), and where a battered, caseless radio was buzzing softly. Refusing cold coffee coldly offered, Kathryn and Dinah locked themselves into the tiny bathroom, while Pasternak and Hobbes crouched outside. Hart and Ed, wordless and wet, played darts down a narrow hallway connecting these chambers, and finally, with only Ketcham and Ben feeling any embarrassment, they trooped out the window again, Hart calling back from among the cans:

'Sure, we understand, sure. You know, we just thought you'd be up, that's all. But say, if you see his connection, see, get an ounce or so for me. We'll cut by again!', all the time sniffing and chuckling to himself, until his words seemed almost a taunt.

They headed for Ketcham's, and the night and the rain had gone. Hobbes and Kathryn left them there, without excuses, withdrawing from exhaustion, while the others went on to the Magnavox, the quart of beer Ketcham hoped might still be there, and a continued resistance to their own sweet fatigue.

The wisdom of their search for some end of the night (the night that was a corridor in which they lurked and groped, believing in a door somewhere, beyond which was a place from which time and the discord bred of time were barred), the wisdom of this seemed to Hobbes, whose mood had changed again, one answer to the reason for being on which Stofsky had once impaled him. But his avowal, even of this strange thought, was motiveless and without intensity.

On the subway, Kathryn slept unashamedly on his shoulder as they sat among the denimed workmen with lunchpails and fresh newspapers, the hurrying, brisk little secretaries who would get their coffee and a Danish downtown and come fully awake only then, and all the other early riders who opened offices, relieved night porters and prepared machines for the first great, groggy wave of the rush hours.

At Seventy-second Street, a merry troup of Girl Scouts, on a hike that would bring them to a picnic's joy, filled the car with their eagerness and their starched scamperings from seat to seat. Some sat, large eyed, hand in hand; others chattered, craning about, open legged, reading all the advertisements to each other; and a little white socked Negro girl was laughing happily as she fiddled with her neighbor's pigtails. In his almost pleasant dullness, Hobbes thought suddenly:

'To be like them or like us, is there another position?'

SEYMOUR KRIM

THE INSANITY BIT

Until this time of complete blast-off in seemingly every department of human life, the idea of insanity was thought of as the most dreadful thing that could happen to a person. Little was actually known about it and the mind conjured up pictures of Bedlam, ninnies walking around in a stupor, a living death that lasted until the poor damned soul's body expired and peace tucked him or her away for eternal keeps. But in this era of monumental need to re-think and re-define almost every former presumption about existence—which has inspired a bombing way of looking at what once were considered the most unbudgeable rocks of reality—the locked door of insanity has been shaken loose and shall yet be hurled wide open. Until one day the prisoners of this definition will walk beside us sharing only the insane plight of mortality itself, which makes quiet madmen of us all.

Every American family has its 'psychotic' cousin or uncle; every friend has wept, prayed, hoped (and finally slid into indifference) for another friend sweating it out in insulin or electric-shock behind the grey walls (public institution) or beyond the clipped roses (private sanitarium). Although my brother, Herbert J. Krim, was institutionalized when I was barely in my 20's—and I co-signed the certificate for a prefrontal lobotomy which ended with his death by hemorrhage on the operating table at Rockland State Hospital—I still had the conventional ideas about insanity that are shared by all 'responsible' readers of *The New York Times*. It is true that as a serious writer I had inherited a great tradition of complete independence and honesty to my actual experience, regardless of what I was supposed to feel; but this was sabotaged by my youth, my ignorance, and an inability to separate my own personal life from a responsibility to question the cliches of experience to their ultimate depth. Like most American writers, from would-be's to celebrities, I was intensely preoccupied by my acutely painful and highly exaggerated subjective image—the Jewish cross, looks, sex, masculinity, a swarm of fears and devices for concealment that were secondary to my decent abilities and serious obligations as a writer intent on telling the truth. In other words: I was too narcissistically and masturbatorially stuck on myself to appreciate the horrible waste of my brother Herbert's death; and with the snotty sense of superiority usually felt by the young American writer, I thought *I* would be forever immune to the judgments of a society which I loftily ignored, or nose-thumbed, without ever coming to grips with on the actual mat of life. Like every creative type of my generation whom I met in my 20's, I was positive I was sanctified, protected by my 'genius,' my flair, my overwhelming ambition.

I was as wrong as you can be and still live to tell about it. In the summer of 1955, when I was 33, the thousand unacknowledged human (not literary!) pressures in my being exploded. I ran barefooted in the streets, spat at members of my family, exposed myself, was almost bodily thrown out of the house of a Nobel Prize-winning author, and believed God had ordained me to act out every conceivable human impulse without an ounce of hypocritical caution. I know today that my instinct was sound, but my reasoning was self-deceptive. It was not God who ordained me, but I who ordained God for my own understandable human purposes. I needed an excuse to force some sort of balance between my bulging inner life and my timid outer behaviour, and I chose the greatest and most comforting symbol of them all. He was my lance and my shield as I tore through the New York streets acting out the bitter rot of a world-full on frustrations that my human nature could no longer lock up. I was finally cornered on the 14th floor of the St. Regis Hotel by two frightened friends and another brother; and with the aid of handcuffs seriously-humorously clipped on by a couple of bobbies I was led off to Bellevue, convinced all along that I was right. I tolerated those who took me away with the kindly condescension of a fake Jesus.

From Bellevue I was soon transferred to a private laughing

academy in Westchester and given insulin-shock treatments. No deep attempt was made to diagnose my 'case'—except the superficial and inaccurate judgment that I had 'hallucinated.' Factually, this was not true; I did not have visual images of people or objects which were not there; I merely believed, with the beautiful relief of absolute justice which the soul of man finds when life becomes unbearable, that God had given me the right and the duty to do everything openly that I had secretly fantasied for years. But this distinction was not gone into by my judges and indifferent captors. They did not have the time, the patience, or even the interest because work in a flip-factory is determined by mathematics: you must find a common denominator of categorization and treatment in order to handle the battalions of miscellaneous humanity that are marched past your desk with high trumpets blowing in their minds.

Like all the other patients, I was considered beyond reasoning with and was treated like a child; not brutally, but efficiently, firmly and patronizingly. In the eyes of this enclosed world I had relinquished my rights as an adult human being. The causes for my explosion were not even superficially examined, nor was the cheek-pinching house psychiatrist— with a fresh flower in the button hole of his fresh daily suit— truly equipped to cope with it even if he had tried, which he did not. Private sanitariums and state institutions, I realized much later, were isolation chambers rather than hospitals in the usual sense; mechanical 'cures' such as the one I underwent in a setup of unchallenged authority, like the Army or a humanitarian prison, slowly brought 75 per cent of the inmates down to a more temporarily modest view of reality. Within nine or ten weeks I too came down, humbled, ashamed, willing to stand up before the class and repeat the middle-class credo of limited expressiveness and the meaning of a dollar in order to get my discharge.

In three months' time I was out, shaken, completely alone, living in a cheap Broadway hotel-room (having been ashamed to go back to Greenwich Village) and going to a conventional Ph.D. psychologist (I had been to three medically-trained therapists in the preceding decade) as a sop to both my conscience and family. I had broken beyond the bounds of 'reality'—a shorthand word which is used by the average psychiatrist for want of the more truthfully complex approach that must eventually accommodate our beings' increasing flights into higher altitudes—and come back to the position I was in before. But once again the causes that had flung me into my own sky continued to eat me up. Sexually unconfident, I went to whores, ate my meals alone, and forced myself to write a few pieces in that loneliest of places, a tiny blank hotel-room in the middle of nowhere. For the first time in my life the incentive to live, the isolation and frustration of my exist-ence, grew dim; while the psychologist smiled and smoked his pipe—and did the well-adjusted, tweedy, urbane act behind his tastefully battered desk as he ladled out platitudes—I was saving up the sleeping bombs, and when I had enough to do the trick I burned the letters I had received through the years from the several men and women I had loved, destroyed my journal of 15 years' standing, and one carefully chosen night went to a hotel in Newark, N.J.

My plan was to take the pills and slowly conk out in the full bathtub, ultimately drowning like Thomas Heggen; if one missed the other would work. I splurged on a beautiful death-room in a modernistic hotel, one that included a bathroom with the biggest tub in the house. But it was too small to fit my long body. The idea of not being able to drown and of surviving the pills afterwards, perhaps to become a burden or an invalid, began to scar what seemed like the paradise of suicide. I went instead to a Polish bar in downtown Newark, vaguely seeking the eternal anodynes of snatch and booze while I mentally played with my fate.

I found the booze and saw a coarse, ignorant Polish girl do such a life-giving, saucy, raucous folk-dance (on the small dance-floor to the right of the bar) that I broke into loving sobs like prayers over my drink. The sun of life blazed from her into my grateful heart. I went back to the beautiful hotel-room, poured the pills down the toilet, and went to sleep. The next morning I returned to Manhattan a chastened man, shaking my head at how close I had come to non-being.

When I told my tale to Mr. Pipe, my psychologist, he speedily hustled me off to a legitimate head-doctor who doped me until a private ambulance came. Very much in my right and one and only mind but too paralyzed by drugs to move, I was once again taken on the long ride —this time to another hedge-trimmed bin in Long Island. I was helpless to protest, mainly because of the shame and guilt I felt for even contemplating suicide. Obviously I was not crazy, mad, psychotic, out of my mind, schizophrenic, paranoiac. I was simply a tormented man-kid who had never steeled himself to face the facts of life—who didn't know what it meant to have principles and live by them come grief or joy—and who thought that human worth and true independence comes as easily as it does in the movies we were all emotionally faked on. As a sputtering fiction-writer and fairly active literary critic, I had had occasional peaks of maturity and illumination; but as a man I was self-deceptive, self-indulgent, crying inwardly for the pleasures of a college-boy even while in my imagination I saw myself as another Ibsen or Dreiser. Ah, the extraordinary mismating of thoughts in the mind of the modern American literary romantic, as fantastic and truly unbelievable a stew of unrelated dreams as have ever been dreamt, believe me!

Once again I was on the human assembly-line: electric shock clubbed my good brain into needless unconsciousness (and I walked to my several executions like a brave little chappie instead of questioning them) and unquestioned Old Testament authority ruled our little club. Good-natured, but mostly cowlike and uneducated male orderlies carried out the orders from above; and apart from the mechanical treatment and the unimaginative grind of occupational therapy, each patient was left completely on his or her bewildered own, a sad and farcical sight when one considered the $125 per week that their frightened families were paying.

I saw now that nine-tenths of the people I was quartered with were not 'insane' by any of the standards a normally intelligent person would use: the majority had lost confidence in their own ability to survive in the world outside, or their families were *afraid* of them and had palmed them off on 'experts,' but positively no serious effort was being made to equip them to become free and independent adults. This was their birthright—beyond country and society, indeed an almost religious obligation—but they were palliated with pills or jolted with shock, their often honest rage echoed back to them as a sign of their 'illness.' Some of them must have been 'sick,' you say. I answer: Who can not be conceived as such in a world so complex ('The truth is there is a truth on every side'—Richard Eberhart) that each group has its own method for judging manners, behaviour, ideas, and finally the worth of human values? What was more important was that I, a person from a hip milieu and with a completely opposite set of values, could see their so-called sickness with the human sensibility that an immersion in literature and experience had given to me—rather than as a clinical manifestation. When I later recognized the objective provinciality of many psychiatrists in precisely the humanistic areas that could cover the actions of the majority of the inmates without finding it 'psychotic,' I realized that the independent thinker and artist today must learn to be resolute towards a subtle, socially powerful godfather who often drips paternalism: namely, the newly-enthroned psychiatric minority that has elevated itself to a dangerous position of 'authority' in the crucial issues of mind, personality, and sanity.

I now began to fight persistently—but still with shakiness—for my release; my life was my own; it did not belong to the cliches of the salesman-aggressive, well-barbered, Jewish refugee (my brother, my enemy!) house psychiatrist or to my smiling, betweeded nonentity of a psychologist, who paid me diplomatically inscrutable visits like a Japanese ambassador. Even if I had been or if there were such a reality as a 'raving maniac'—which, perhaps childishly, I implore the over-imaginative, zeitgeist-vulnerable reader to believe is an impossible conception today—I would and should have fought for my release. What the institution-spared layman does not realize is that a sensitive and multiple-reacting human being remains the same everywhere, including a sanitarium, and such an environment can duplicate the injustice or vulgarity which drove your person there in the first place. By this I mean that a mental hospital is not an asylum or a sanctuary in the old-fashioned sense: it is just a roped-off side-street of modern existence, rife with as many contradictions, half-truths and lousy architecture as life itself.

Both of the sanitariums I was in were comparable to Grossinger's, in that they took in only financially comfortable, conventionally middle-class, non-intellectual people. By every human standard my being there was life's sarcastic answer to whatever romantic ideas I had about justice. Since the age of 19 I had deliberately led an existence of experimentation, pursuit of truth, bohemianism, and non-commercialism: fate's punishment for my green naivete was for me to recover my supposed mental health in this atmosphere of uncriticizable authority, air-conditioned by just the whiffs of truth that are perfumed and bland, and based on a pillar of middle-class propriety with the cut-throat reality of money underneath. Could I accept my former life, which had produced some good work, as a lie to myself—which the house-psychiatrist wanted me to do (in effect) in his one psycho-therapeutic pass at me (he left me alone after this)? I could not and never would: not only for myself but for the great principles and accomplishments of others, both living and dead, which had been my guide throughout my adult life. I might fail—but why go on having an identity at all if in a crisis you will throw away not only your past years, but the moral achievements of rare souls who have shared in your emotional and intellectual experience and whose own contributions to existence are also at stake?

When I heard this second house-psychiatrist literally equate sanity with the current cliches of adjustment and describe Greenwich Village as a 'psychotic community,' I saw with clarity that *insanity* and *psychosis* can no longer be respected as meaningful definitions—but are used by limited individuals in positions of social power to describe ways of behaving and thinking that are alien, threatening, and *obscure* to them. (A year later when I took a psychiatrist friend of mine to the

San Remo, she told me with a straight face that it reminded her of the 'admission ward in Bellevue,' where she had interned. This was her analogy on the basis of accurate but limited experience, that increasing chasm which separates intelligent people from understanding each other. I realized with a sense of almost incommunicable hopelessness that the gap between her and the well-known poet with whom I had had a beer at the Remo two weeks before was tremendous, and that between these two poles of intelligence the neutral person—who could see the logic of each—was being mashed up with doubt and conflict. The poet was at home, or at least the heat was off, there; while the psychiatrist felt alien and had made a contemptuous psycho-sociological generalization. There was little bond of shared values and therefore genuine communication between both of these intelligent and honest human beings, each of whom contributed to my life.)

To finish with my four months in the sanitarium: I argued and reasoned for the basic right to the insecurity of freedom, and finally a good friend did the dirty in-fighting of getting me out. Had I to do it over again, I believe I would now have the guts to threaten such an institution or psychologist with a law suit, ugly as such a procedure can be to a person already vulnerable with the hash-marks of one legally defined 'psychotic episode' and the contemplation of the criminal act of suicide. But I had been—as so many of Jack Kerouac's subterraneans are when faced with the machinery of official society—milk and sawdust when, in such situations, you must be iron and stone in spite of your own frailty. It is not that the present-day authorities of mental life want to railroad anyone, as in your Grade C horror movie; it is merely that as one grows older it becomes clear that there are almost unremediable differences between people in the total outlook towards life.

Mine had hardened as a result of my experiences, and I realized it was better to die out in the world, if need be, than be deprived of the necessity to confront existence behind the cheap authority of a lock and key. The majority of people who stay in mental institutions for any length of time do not want to return to the uncertain conditions outside the walls: which in our time spells out to emotionally anarchic, multi-dimensional, brain-trying, anxiety-loaded, and—O hear me mortality, from the year one!—ultimate and divine life.

I returned downtown—to the very Village that I heard the psychiatrist place deep in Freudian Hell, with that pious over-extension of terminology which reveals a limited private morality behind the use of so-called scientific language—and tried to tenderly pick up the threads of my former social life. I saw that my closest and most brilliant friends did not really understand, or were afraid to understand, the contemporary insanity bit. Almost all of them had been soul-whirled by psycho-therapy at some time, and each had the particularly contemporary fear of insanity which has become the psycho-logical H-bomb of city life; in theory they may have granted that insanity was no longer the uniform horror it seems to the inexperienced imagination—like a spook in the night—but centuries of inherited fear, plus the daily crises of 1950's living, made them emotionally cautious about seeing my experience as merely an *extension* of their own.

One, a poet-philosopher whom I admire, clapped me on the back and said with some literary awe that I had 'returned from the dead, like Lazarus.' This struck me as greatly melo-dramatic, untruthful, and saddening because intellectuals and especially artists should be the very people to understand that insanity today is a matter of definition, not fact; that there can no longer be a fixed criterion, just as there is no longer a reality like that described by Allen Ginsberg in 'Howl' (an exciting achievement), where he sees 'the best minds of my generation destroyed by madness.'

I believe this is lurid sentimentality. Ginsberg may have seen the most gifted people of his generation destroyed by an *interpretation* of madness, which is a much more real threat in a time of such infinite, moon-voyaging extension to experi-ence that the validly felt act is often fearfully jailed in a window-less cell of definition by hard-pressed authorities, whose very moral axis is in danger of toppling. Madness today is a literary word; insanity is a dated legal conception as rigid as an Ibsen play; and 'psychosis,' the antiseptic modern word that sends chills down the ravines of my friends' minds, has become so weakened (despite its impressive white-jacketed look) by narrow-minded, square, and fast-slipping ideological preconceptions that it must be held at arm's length, like a dead rat, for any cool understanding. When this is done, I believe you will see that the word and the state of mind it tries to fix are subject to the gravest questioning; much of which centers around the amount of freedom either permitted to human expression or, more important, what it must take for itself to live in this time when such *unfamiliar* demands are made on the being. Norms crack when they can no longer fight back the content that spills over cookie-mold conceptions of 'sane' behavior—and they must be elasticized to stretch around the new bundle of life.

Two weeks before I was back walking down 8th Street a gratefully free neurotic, I had been thought of in the minds of compassionate, but uninformed, friends as a fairly wild-eyed psychotic. The mere fact that I had been in a sanitarium had pulled a curtain of emotional blindness down over my friends' vision; and yet I was the same person I had been when I entered the happy-house. The unexamined fear of an 'insanity' which no longer exists as a framed picture conventionalizes the very people who should view this now only *symbolic* word with clear, unafraid, and severely skeptical eyes. I had not been among 'the dead'—unless killing time looking at 'Gunsmoke' and Jackie Gleason on TV, playing bridge, and reading Tolstoy and Nathanael West is considered death. I had not been 'destroyed by madness,' Mr. Ginsberg!—in fact, the act of incarceration made me realize how significant (indeed indelible) individual freedom is, and thus helped brick-and-mortar my point of view rather than destroy it. When I was once again semi-knit into a way of life in my new Village home, I discovered that other writers and intellectuals whom I knew had also undergone the sanitarium or mental-hospital holiday, but had kept mum because of indecision as to how frankly one should confess such a stigma.

I understood their practical caution, but discovered that they lived in a sewer-light of guilt, fear and throat-gagging anxiety, instead of openly and articulately coping with the monster of doubt. 'Do you think I'm sane?' is the question I ultimately began to hear from these brilliant people (one scarred tribesman to another!) who had been intimidated into denying the worth of their most pregnant ideas, the very ones that create *new concrete standards of sanity* or *sense* in a time that has emotionally, if not yet officially, out-lived the abstractions of the past. For myself—although uncertain as to how expressive I should be, even with the very intellectuals I had always considered my brothers in a completely free inquiry into every nook and cranny of life—the problem was suddenly answered when a gifted young writer told a charming hostess I had just met that I had been in 'two insane asylums.'

I was pierced and hurt, not because I actually considered my supposed nuttiness a yellow badge of dishonor, but because the writer in question had ducked out from under his own experience (which I instinctively knew included some of the crises which had launched me upon the streets like a human missile) and pretended such melodrama was foreign to him. I was appalled because I thought that of all people my fellow highbrow writers should be the first to understand and concede the universal nature of the blows that had felled me in the eyes of official society. But I was wrong. There are spikes on the truth which are so close to the slashed heart of contemporary mortality that men and women will lie and refuse acknowledgment, even when it is necessary to the survival of others; they forfeit their humanhood and final worth to life by doing this, but even in the small band of the avant-garde the pursuit of the truth is given up with that weak excuse: 'a sense of reality.'

After this turncoat put-down by a member of my own club, so to speak, there was no longer any issue for myself. I could not live with the squirming burden of secretiveness because my personal history had become public gossip in the small Village group I traveled with. After snake-bitten laughter at my own romantically cultivated simple-mindedness in thinking my fall would be taken with the hip sophistication I had truly expected, I was glad I had become a stooge or victim; because

135

I basically knew that I had played a juicy part in a contemporary American morality play that is going to do standing-room nightly until its implications are understood. We live in what for the imaginative person are truly hallucinated times, because there is more life on every side—and the possibility of conceiving this surplus in a dizzying multitude of ways—than our inheritance and equipment enables us to deal with. My type and perhaps your type of person only *acted out* what other less passionate people feel, but do not express. A 'breakdown' such as mine can therefore be learned from:

The first thing one can see is that the isolating of a person saves his or her friends and family from being embarrassed (trivial as this seems, it is a nasty factor in institutionalization), perhaps hurt, and theoretically stops the 'sick' person from doing something irreparable while in the grip of the furies. Seen this way, the enforced shackling of an individual seems sad but reasonable. But contemporary adults, however disturbed (often with justice!), are not children; there is doubt in my mind whether we have any right, other than blunt self-interest, to impose our so-called humanitarian wishes on another to the degree where we jail them in order to save them. I must illustrate this with my own case. When I was considered out of my mind during my original upward thrust into the sheer ecstasy of 100 per cent uninhibitedness, I was aware of the 'daringness' of my every move; it represented at heart an existential *choice* rather than a mindless discharge. It could not be tolerated by society, and I was punished for it, but my 'cure' was ultimately a chastisement, *not a medical healing process*. In my own exhibitionistic and self-dramatizing way, when I flipped, I was nevertheless instinctively rebelling against a fact which I think is objectively true in our society and time: and that is the lack of alignment between an immense inner world and an outer one which has not yet legalized, or officially recognized, the forms that can tolerate the flood of communication from the mind to the stage of action.

Traditionally, it was always taught that the artistic person could work out his or her intense private life by expressing it on the easel or typewriter. In faded theory this seems reasonable, but with the billionaire's wealth of potential human experience both fore, aft and sideways in the world today, it is abnormal not to want to participate more Elizabethanly in this over-abundant life. The hunchbacked joy the artist once may have had in poring over the objects of his interest, and then putting the extract into his work, can no longer be honestly sufficient to the most human hearts today. There has arisen an overwhelming need for the highly imaginative spirit (based on the recognition that the mere mind of man can no longer lock up the volume of its experience) to forge a bridge so that the bursting galaxy of this inner world can be received in actual public life. But there is such a time-lag between our literally amazing subjective life—which has imaginings of a powerful altitude equal to the heaven-exploring freedom of privacy—and the mummery of outer behavior, that when the contemporary imaginator expresses his genuine thoughts in public he often feels that he has exposed himself beyond redemption. Room has not yet been made by those who dominate social power for the natural outward show of the acrobatic thinking that ceaselessly swings in the surrealistic minds of our most acute contemporaries. Put crudely but simply, a bookish notion of what constitutes 'normality' in this supremely a-normal age drives the liveliest American sensibilities back into the dungeon of self—creating pressures which must maim the soul one way or another—rather than understanding that the great need today is for imagination to come gloriously out in the open, and shrink the light-years that separate the mind from external life. (Trying to fill this need is, hands-down, one of the significant accomplishments of the beats—in my opinion—no matter what defensive moralists say; the raw junk that they have peddled under a Kotex flag of liberation is a different matter, which doesn't rightly fit in here.)

It was trying to close this distance between Me and Thou, between externality and the mind, that I was instinctively attempting when I cut loose with my natural, suffocating self in 1955 upon the taboo grounds of outer life. I could stand unfulfilled desire no longer. Thus it is my conviction today that ideals of social behavior must squat down and broaden to the point where they can both absorb and see the necessity for 'aberrations' that were once, squarely and Teddy Rooseveltianly, regarded as pathological. The imagination of living human beings, not dead gods, must be openly embodied if there is to be some rational connection between what people actually are and what they are permitted to show. But as with every significant change in meaning, such acts of expressiveness will cost blood before they will be tolerated and understood by psychiatrists, sociologists, the law, police, and all other instruments of social force. Ironically, it is the very 'psychotics' in institutions who have unwittingly done the most to initiate a bigger and more imaginative conception of what constitutes *meaningful* behavior. By dealing with people imprisoned in this category, the most perceptive laymen and psychiatrists are beginning to see symbolic meanings where before they saw flat irrationality, because their approach was literal (as if anyone who had the imagination to go 'mad' would be stuffy enough to act in prose!). It is then borne in upon them, out of common sense and humility, that a much more expanded conception of what is 'sane' is a prerequisite to doing justice to the real emotional state of human beings today; not the abstract theorems of a clean Euclidian conception, but the real, harsh, multiple, often twisted, on-again, off-again, mishmash of the so-called normal mind. One can say without pretense that the pioneering 'psychotic' is the human poet of the future; and the most imaginative, least tradition-bound psychiatrists are now playing the role of New Critics, learning to closely read the difficult and unexpected meanings of what formerly were thought of as obscure—in fact, off-limits— warpings of humanity.

In my own case I was brought face-to-face because of my trial by shock (both electric and the human aftermath) with a crucial reality which I had long dodged. It can be put approximately this way: A serious artist-type must in the present environment, as always—cliches have a way of becoming profundities when you have to live them!—literally fight for survival, if he or she is going to embody the high traditions that originally made the hot pursuit of truth through art the greatest kick in their lives. But to follow this ideal today is tougher than perhaps it has ever been before; and there are specific reasons why. Foremost is the increasing loss of position for the poet (the artist incarnate) as 'the unacknowledged legislator of the race' in a period when the terrifying bigness of society makes the average person resort to more immediate and practical oracles (psychiatrists, sociologists, chemists) than to the kind of imaginative truth that the artist can give. Secondly, the artist-type in our mass society is no longer 'privileged' in any way, if indeed he ever was; by this I mean that the laws and shibboleths of the huge democratic tribe judge him as severely as they do the shoemaker next door. Whatever pampering the serious artist once received has become a laugh in our time, when everyone is hustling on approximately the same level for success, lovers, status, money, headlines, thrills, security—for everything.

The emergence of an emotionally mutinous democracy has upset the old categories and cast us all into the boiling sea of naked existence, without the props of class, or profession, or the certainty about one's worth as judged by the seemingly clear-cut hierarchies of the past. While, in my opinion, this should be sizzlingly beautiful to every true artist-type, because it is adventurous in the highest conceivable and most mortally dangerous sense, it is also full of the most sinking fears and doubts. For example: can the intelligent writer, painter or composer—the individual with a view of life all his own, which he believes to be true—be indifferent to the prevailing social climate and risk everything by sticking to a viewpoint which will bring him into conflict with the most *normal* (shared by the most people) human emotions in a mass society? (Tag him with the label of 'insanity,' estrangement from the tempting pie of regular-guy and regular-gal American experience, bring him the isolating fate of being misunderstood even by the 'enlightened,' and regarded as a personal challenge by others who have made an uneasy truce.)

This is a very serious problem and entails a bigger threat than in the past. Since the artist-type can no longer be realistically

139

considered as being 'outside' our definition of society or human nature—and must in this country above all others be seen within the circle of a mass-democratic humanity, for that is where his final strength probably lies—his defections will be judged by those in positions of social power as fluky aberrations *no different from anyone else's*. He will be judged and penalized by the same standards; and in a majority of cases, from what I have seen, his will and stamina are broken (or rationalized into loose harness) and his point of view changed. Frankly, for the artist-type in our environment there is no longer any solid ground whatever under his feet—anything solid he possesses must be won from air and shaped by fanatical resoluteness. For all is open to question today, is a gamble, and has none of the 'official' security of the acknowledged professions or even any semblance of unity within his own field. It is for such reasons that the genuine artist-thinker is in such an unenviable and peculiar position in America right now. He is of society and yet, by instinct and inheritance, apart from it: therefore he has to clarify his position in his own mind to a menthol-sharp degree if he wants to survive with intactness, because, as I've tried to show, he will be crushed subtly or conclusively unless he separates his eternal role in society from the onrush of personal doubt that every human being worth the name lives with today.

I learned as a result of my far-out public exhibition, and the manhandling that followed, to distrust the definitions of crude social authority as they pertained to myself and my friends, who share a generally akin point of view and are all either professionals or semi-professionals in the arts and intellectual life. We can not be skimmed off the top and bracketed as thinly as I had been diagnosed at Bellevue; and the psychiatrists who impatiently felt for the bumps within my head, while presumably competent at a human-machine level, are not as a group sensitive, informed or sympathetic enough with my purposes in life to be of help. In fact, in a basic way they must be my defining opposition in history (daily life) while my friends beyond time (the ideal)—if that doesn't read too pretentiously. It was a sharp revelation for me to learn this as a result of my on-your-hands-and-knees, boy! defeat with authority. As I confessed before, like so many confused young Americans puttering around in the arts, I had phonily pumped into my serious intentions the gassiest dreams of what the struggle for ideas truly is, of false and sentimentalized views of authority (both bowing before it and blow-hard defiance), and in general acted more like a Hollywood caricature of a 'genius' than a person with the ballbreaking desire to uphold the immortal flame of art in his smallish hand.

I found after I had been handcuffed, ambulanced, doped, needled, marched in formation and given a leather belt to make as if I were in my dotage rather than the prime of life, that I *had to* disagree basically and deliberately with the cowardly normal notion of what constitutes insanity because it is only by *the assertion of the individual spirit that we can change definitions of reality that are already insecure and losing their hold on the conceptual imagination.* In other words, if a majority of people agrees that what was once confidently called insanity does not exist *as such*, can not truthfully be a determining measurement in a time like this where each good person in the reaches of his mind is often an amateur lunatic by older slogans of 'rationality,' then the enslavement of the word and meaning are broken. Not only was I forced to this simple attitude because my human spirit refused the reduction of my total self to only one exaggerated aspect of it—namely the pathological label—I saw in both sanitariums no consistency in what was thought of as 'sick.'

In short, I could no longer afford to think of contemporary insanity as an exact objective phenomenon, like thunder or cancer, but rather as an interpretation of human thought and behavior conditioned by inherited prejudices, fear, questionable middle-class assumptions of the purpose of life, a policeman's narrow idea of freedom, and dollar-hard AMA notions of responsibility and *expediency* ('1. Apt and suitable to the end in view; as, an expedient solution; hence, advantageous. 2. Conducive to special advantage rather than to what is universally right.'—Web. New Colleg. Dict.). No longer could I see any true authority or finality in a conception that could be too

141

conveniently tailored to fit the situation. I knew then that anyone who dares the intellectual conventions of this local time must be prepared to have 'psychotic' or any of its variants— paranoid, schizophrenic, even the mild psychopathic!— thrown at them. The pathological interpretation of human nature has become a style in our period (overemphasized by the junior science of psychiatry) and has come to mirror the fears, anxieties and values of those currently in positions of social authority more often than the person who is being gutted. Within the iron maiden of this fashion—which undeniably hurts, right down to the roots of the soul—the independent person and the artist-type have no choice but to trust implicitly what they see with their intellect and imagination; for when the climate changes, only the individual vision will stand secure upon its God-given legs of having had faith in actual experience.

I therefore believe that the fear and even the actual living through of much that is called 'insanity' is almost an emotional necessity for every truly feeling, reacting, totally human person in America at this time—*until* he or she passes through the soul-crippling (not healing) judgment of such language and comes out of the fire at the point where other words and hence different conceptions are created from the wounds. The psychiatric vocabulary and definitions, which once seemed such a liberating instrument for modern man, have now woven a tight and ironically strangling noose around the neck of the brain; but we can be grateful that the human soul is so constructed that it ultimately bursts concepts once held as true out of its terrible need to live and creates the world anew in order to breathe in it. One final thought: should any readers see this article as an effort at self-justification they are right, as far as they go; but they should remember that it is only out of the self and its experience (even if I have failed here) that new light has ever been cast on the perpetual burden of making life ever more *possible* at its most crucial level.

COMMENTARY

JOHN CLELLON HOLMES

THE PHILOSOPHY OF THE BEAT GENERATION

Last September [1957] a novel was published which The New York *Times* called 'the most beautifully executed, the clearest and most important utterance' yet made by a young writer; a book likely to represent the present generation, it said, as *The Sun Also Rises* represents the Twenties. It was called *On The Road*, by Jack Kerouac, and it described the experiences and attitudes of a restless group of young Americans, 'mad to live, mad to talk, mad to be saved,' whose primary interests seemed to be fast cars, wild parties, modern jazz, sex, marijuana, and other miscellaneous 'kicks.' Kerouac said they were members of a Beat Generation. As spokesman for his movement, Kerouac suddenly found himself, to his consternation, in the midst of a blazing controversy. Newspaper reporters trailed after him; critics, following their initial reviews, continued to parody or praise him; and, on one television interview, a fascinated New York audience heard scraps of an almost unintelligible conversation that went something like this:

INTERVIEWER: 'You said—half-kiddingly—that you have been on a two-day drunk.'

KEROUAC: 'Well, I haven't been on a two-day drunk—I've been *drinking* for two days.'

And: INTERVIEWER: 'This beat generation has been described as a "seeking" generation. What are you looking for?'

KEROUAC: 'God. I want God to show me His face.'

No one seemed to know exactly what Kerouac meant, and, indeed, some critics insisted that these wild young hedonists were not really representative of anything, but were only 'freaks,' 'mental and moral imbeciles,' 'bourgeois rebels.' Nevertheless, something about the book, and something about the term, would not be so easily dismissed. The book became the object of heated discussion, selling well as a consequence;

and the term stuck—at least in the craw of those who denied there was any such thing.

What Kerouac seemed to offer was at least some insight into the attitudes of a generation whose elders were completely flabbergasted. Implicitly, rock and roll, dope addiction, juvenile delinquency, an amoral attitude toward sex and all the attendant phenomena that have characterized the modern young American in extreme seemed to be the primary preoccupation of Kerouac's characters.

Providing a word that crystallizes the characteristics of an entire generation has always been a thankless task. If postwar generations seem to demand one more than others, perhaps it is because the members of a postwar generation have in common an unusually unifying experience, shared at an impressionable age. But to find a word that will describe the group that is now roughly between the ages of eighteen and twenty-eight (give or take a year in either direction) is even more difficult, because this group includes veterans of three distinct kinds of modern war: a hot war, a cold war, and a war that was stubbornly not called a war at all, but a police action.

Some years ago, *Time* Magazine called them the Silent Generation, but this may have been because *Time* was not really listening. Others tried out the Waiting Generation, and the Go Generation, but all of these were somehow inadequate. Now, with the word 'beat,' we may have their sobriquet at last. Everyone who has lived through a war, any sort of war, knows that beat means, not so much weariness, as rawness of the nerves; not so much being 'filled up to *here*,' as being emptied out. It describes a state of mind from which all unessentials have been stripped, leaving it receptive to everything around it, but impatient with trivial obstructions. To be beat is to be at the bottom of your personality, looking up; to be existential in the Kierkegaard, rather than the Jean-Paul Sartre, sense.

What differentiated the characters in *On The Road* from the slum-bred petty criminals and icon-smashing Bohemians which have been something of a staple in much modern American fiction—what made them *beat* —was something which seemed to irritate critics most of all. It was Kerouac's insistence that actually they were on a quest, and that the specific object of their quest was spiritual. Though they rushed back and forth across the country on the slightest pretext, gathering kicks along the way, their real journey was inward; and if they seemed to trespass most boundaries, legal and moral, it was only in the hope of finding a belief on the other side. 'The Beat Generation,' he said, 'is basically a religious generation.' And later, in another interview, Kerouac amplified: 'This includes anyone from fifteen to fifty-five who digs *everything*. We're not Bohemian, remember. Beat means beatitude, not beat up. You *feel* this. You feel it in a beat, in jazz—real cool jazz or a good gutty rock number.'

On the face of it, this may seem absurd when you consider that parents, civic leaders, law-enforcement officers, and even literary critics most often have been amused, irritated or downright shocked by the behavior of this generation. They have noted more delinquency, more excess, more social irresponsibility in it than in any generation in recent years, and they have seen less interest in politics, community activity, and the orthodox religious creeds. They have been outraged by the adulation of the late James Dean, seeing in it signs of a dangerous morbidity, and they have been equally outraged by the adulation of Elvis Presley, seeing in it signs of a dangerous sensuality. They have read statistics on narcotics addiction, sexual promiscuity, and the consumption of alcohol among the young—and blanched. They have lamented the fact that 'the most original (literary) work being done in this country has come to depend on the bizarre and the offbeat for its creative stimulus'; and they have expressed horror at the disquieting kind of juvenile crime—violent and without an object—which has erupted in most large cities.

They see no signs of a search for spiritual values in a generation whose diverse tragic heroes have included jazzman Charlie Parker, actor Dean and poet Dylan Thomas; and whose interests have ranged all the way from bebop to rock and roll; from hipsterism to Zen Buddhism; from vision-inducing drugs to Method Acting. To be told that this is a generation whose almost exclusive concern is the discovery of something in which to believe seems to them to fly directly in the face of all the evidence.

And yet, though everyone who reads the newspapers, looks at television or goes to the movies is probably well-acquainted with the behavior of the Beat Generation, very little attention has been given to the attitudes behind that behavior. And this despite the fact that it is what people think, and not only what they do, which gives us a glimpse of the way they are.

Perhaps all generations feel that they have inherited 'the worst of all possible worlds,' but the Beat Generation probably has more claim to the feeling than any that have come before it. The historical climate which formed its attitudes was violent, and it did as much violence to ideas as it did to the men who believed in them. One does not have to be consciously aware of such destruction to feel it. Conventional notions of private and public morality have been steadily atrophied in the last ten or fifteen years by the exposure of treason in government, corruption in labor and business, and scandal among the mighty of Broadway and Hollywood. The political faiths which sometimes seem to justify slaughter have become steadily less appealing as slaughter has reached proportions that stagger even the mathematical mind. Orthodox religious conceptions of good and evil seem increasingly inadequate to explain a world of science-fiction turned fact, past-enemies turned bosom-friends, and honorable-diplomacy turned brink-of-war. Older generations may be distressed or cynical or apathetic about this world, or they may have somehow adjusted their conceptions to it. But the Beat Generation is specifically the *product* of this world, and it is the only world its members have ever known.

It is the first generation in American history that has grown up with peacetime military training as a fully accepted fact of life. It is the first generation for whom the catch phrases of psychiatry have become such intellectual pabulum that it can dare to think they may not be the final yardstick of the human soul. It is the first generation for whom genocide, brain-washing, cybernetics, motivational research—and the resultant limitation of the concept of human volition which is inherent in them—have been as familiar as its own face. It is also the first generation that has grown up since the possibility of the nuclear destruction of the world has become the final answer to all questions.

But instead of the cynicism and apathy which accompanies the end of ideals, and which gave the Lost Generation a certain poetic, autumnal quality, the Beat Generation is altogether too vigorous, too intent, too indefatigable, too curious to suit its elders. Nothing seems to satisfy or interest it but extremes, which, if they have included the criminality of narcotics, have also included the sanctity of monasteries. Everywhere the Beat Generation seems occupied with the feverish production of answers—some of them frightening, some of them foolish—to a single question: how are we to live? And if this is not immediately recognizable in leather-jacketed motorcyclists and hipsters 'digging the street,' it is because we assume that only answers which recognize man as a collective animal have any validity; and do not realize that this generation cannot conceive of the question in any but personal terms, and knows that the only answer it can accept will come out of the dark night of the individual soul.

If Hemingway and Fitzgerald wrote the books of the Lost Generation, they also lived its life (the hard-drinking, expatriate life of desperate hilarity and tough cynicism), and Kerouac has done no less with his generation. Years ago, after an earlier novel was published and he became absorbed in New York's literary life for a time, he told me in disgust: 'I have to make my choice between all *this* and the rattling trucks on the American road. And I think I'll choose the rattling trucks, where I don't have to explain anything, and where nothing is explained, only *real.*' He has stuck by that choice ever since. What followed it were years of a nomad existence—hitchhiking, odd jobs, stretches of writing in San Francisco, Denver, New York and Mexico ('Ah, John, Ernest Hemingway was wrong, and how could any of us have known, not having seen a bullfight'). What followed was the discovery of a new attitude which young people everywhere shared to some extent.

By the time *On The Road* was finally published, he knew the underside of America (its highways and its hipsters) as perhaps no writer before him has ever known it; and now he is no longer interested in 'explaining' his generation in chilly sociological and psychological terms. He knows that its truth lies elsewhere. He has heard the feverish talk in the speeding car; he has seen the young, flushed faces turned intently toward the tenor-saxman; he can say of most older literary attitudes: 'Life goes on. . . . In the backstreets of Philadelphia, men listen to the Phillies game and then go out and kill their wives. In the streets of Baltimore, all alike with white doorsteps, someone is genuinely and seriously dying. . . . So it is only our *writings* that are storming in a teacup, and not the world.'

On his travels, he meets hitchhikers who are writing 'crazy novels' and rucksack poets bumming toward 'another coast' to read their poems to friends, and out of their perceptions, he feels, literature will eventually come. And when it does, it will be the literature of a Beat Generation.

Before looking at some of the answers that literature will attempt to provide, it would be well to remember what Norman Mailer, in a recent article on the hipster, said about the hip language: 'What makes (it) a special language is that it cannot really be taught—if one shares none of the experiences of elation and exhaustion which it is equipped to describe, then it seems merely arch or vulgar or irritating.' This is also true to a large extent of the whole reality in which the members of the Beat Generation have grown. If you can't see it the way they do, you can't understand the way they act. One way to see it, perhaps the easiest, is to investigate the image they have of themselves.

A large proportion of this generation lived vicariously in the short, tumultuous career of actor James Dean. He was their idol in much the same way that Valentino was the screen idol of the Twenties, and Clark Gable was the screen idol of the Thirties. But there was a differance, and it was *all* the difference. In Dean, they saw not a daydream Lothario who was more attractive, mysterious and wealthy than they were, or a virile man of action with whom they could fancifully identify to make up for their own feelings of powerlessness, but a wistful, reticent youth, looking over the abyss separating him from older people with a level, saddened eye; living intensely in alternate explosions of tenderness and violence; eager for love and a sense of purpose, but able to accept them only on terms which acknowledged the facts of life as he knew them: in short, themselves.

To many people, Dean's mumbling speech, attenuated silences, and rash gestures seemed the ultimate in empty mannerisms, but the young generation knew that it was not so much that he was inarticulate or affected as it was he was unable to believe in some of the things his scripts required him to say. He spoke to them right through all the expensive make-believe of million-dollar productions, saying with his sighs, and the prolonged shifting of his weight from foot to foot: 'Well, I suppose there's no way out of this, but we know how it *really* is. . . .' They knew he was lonely, they knew he was flawed, they knew he was confused. But they also knew that he 'dug,' and so they delighted in his sloppy clothes and untrimmed hair and indifference to the proprieties of fame. He was not what they wanted to be; he was what they *were*. He lived hard and without complaint; and he died as he lived, going fast. Or as Kerouac's characters express it:

'We gotta go and never stop going till we get there.'

'Where we going, man?'

'I don't know, but we gotta go.'

Only the most myopic, it seems to me, can view this need for mobility (and it is one of the distinguishing characteristics of the Beat Generation) as a flight rather than a search.

Dean was the product of an acting discipline known as The Method (taught at New York's Actors Studio), which has proved irresistibly attractive to young actors and has filled the screens and stages of America in recent years with laconic, slouching youths, who suddenly erupt with such startling jets of emotional power that the audience is left as shaken and moved as if it had overheard a confession. The primary concern of

151

The Method is to find the essence of a character, his soul, and the actor is encouraged to do this by utilizing emotions in his own experience that correspond to those in the script. Non-Method actors sometimes complain that disciples of The Method coast along during the greater part of a role, hoarding their emotional resources for the climactic scenes. To which Method actors might reply that only the climactic scenes in most plays and movies have any deep human truth to them, and that the rest is only empty dialogue building toward the moment when the character reveals himself.

An example of this might well be the movie *On The Waterfront*, conceived by its writer, Budd Schulberg, and its director, Elia Kazan, as a social exposé of conditions among longshoremen, centralized in the figure of a young ex-boxer mixed up in a corrupt union. Marlon Brando's electrifying performance of this role, however, so interiorized the character that the social overtones seemed insignificant beside the glimpse of a single human soul caught in the contradictions and absurdity of modern life. It was exactly as if Brando were saying in scene after scene: 'Man is not merely a social animal, a victim, a product. At the bottom, man is a spirit.' As a theory of acting keyed to this proposition, The Method is pre-eminently the acting style of the Beat Generation.

Critics constantly express amazement at the willingness, even the delight, with which this generation accepts what are (to the critics) basically unflattering images of itself. It was noticed, for instance, that the most vociferous champions of the film, *The Wild Ones* (which gave a brutal, unsympathetic account of the wanton pillage of a California town by a band of motorcyclists), were the motorcyclists themselves. Equally, most juvenile delinquents probably saw, and approved of, the portrait of themselves offered in *Rebel Without a Cause*, even though they laughed at the social-worker motivations for their conduct that filled the script. One can only conclude that what they see and what adults see are two different things. The standards by which adults judge the behavior portrayed have scant reality to them, for these standards are based on social and moral values that do not take into consideration their dilemma, which might be described as the will to believe even in the face of the inability to do so in conventional terms.

All too often older people make the mistake of concluding that what lies beneath this is an indifference to values of any kind, whereas almost the reverse is true. Even the crudest and most nihilistic memeber of the Beat Generation, the young slum hoodlum, is almost exclusively concerned with the problem of belief, albeit unconsciously. It seems incredible that no one has realized that the only way to make the shocking juvenile murders coherent at all is to understand that they are specifically moral crimes. The youth, who last summer stabbed another youth and was reported to have said to his victim, 'Thanks a lot, I just wanted to know what it felt like,' was neither insane nor perverted. There was no justification for his crime, either in the hope of gain or in the temporary hysteria of hate, or even in the egotism of a Loeb and Leopold, who killed only to prove they could get away with it. His was the sort of crime envisaged by the Marquis De Sade a hundred and fifty years ago—a crime which the cruel absence of God made obligatory if a man were to prove that he was a man and not a mere blot of matter. Such crimes, which are no longer rarities and which are all committed by people under twenty-five, cannot be understood if we go on mouthing the same old panaceas about broken homes and slum environments and bad company, for they are spiritual crimes, crimes against the identity of another human being, crimes which reveal with stark and terrifying clarity the lengths to which a desperate need for values can drive the young. For in actuality it is the *longing* for values which is expressed in such a crime, and not the hatred of them. It is the longing to do or feel something meaningful, and it provides a sobering glimpse of how completely the cataclysms of this century have obliterated the rational, humanistic view of Man on which modern society has been erected.

The reaction to this on the part of young people, even those in a teen-age gang, is not a calculated immorality, however, but a return to an older, more personal, but no less rigorous code of ethics, which includes the inviolability of comradeship,

153

the respect for confidences, and an almost mystical regard for courage—all of which are the ethics of the tribe, rather than the community; the code of a small compact group living in an indifferent or a hostile environment, which it seeks not to conquer or change, but only to elude.

On a slightly older level, this almost primitive will to survive gives rise to the hipster, who moves through our cities like a member of some mysterious, nonviolent Underground, not plotting anything, but merely keeping alive an unpopular philosophy, much like the Christian of the first century. He finds in bop, the milder narcotics, his secretive language and the night itself, affirmation of an individuality (more and more besieged by the conformity of our national life), which can sometimes only be expressed by outright eccentricity. But his aim is to be asocial, not antisocial; his trancelike 'digging' of jazz or sex or marijuana is an effort to free *himself*, not exert power over others. In his most enlightened state, the hipster feels that argument, violence and concern for attachments are ultimately Square, and he says, 'Yes, man, yes!' to the Buddhist principle that most human miseries arise from these emotions. I once heard a young hipster exclaim wearily to the antagonist in a barroom brawl: 'Oh, man, you don't want to interfere with him, with his kick. I mean, man, what a *drag!*'

On this level, the hipster practices a kind of passive resistance to the Square society in which he lives, and the most he would ever propose as a program would be the removal of every social and intellectual restraint to the expression and enjoyment of his unique individuality, and the 'kicks' of 'digging' life through it. And, as Norman Mailer said in the afore-quoted article, 'The affirmation implicit in (this) proposal is that man would then prove to be more creative than murderous, and so would not destroy himself.' Which is, after all, a far more spiritual, or even religious, view of human nature than that held by many of those who look at this Beat Generation and see only its excesses.

This conviction of the creative power of the unfettered individual soul stands behind everything in which the members of this generation interest themselves. If they are curious about drugs, for instance, their initial reason is as much the desire to tap the unknown world inside themselves as to escape from the unbearable world outside. 'But, man, last night,' they will say, 'I got so high I knew *everything*. I mean, I knew *why*.'

In the arts, modern jazz is almost exclusively the music of the Beat Generation, as poetry (at least until Kerouac's novel) is its literature. If the members of this generation attend to a wailing sax in much the same way as men once used to attend the words and gestures of sages, it is because jazz is primarily the music of inner freedom, of improvisation, of the creative individual rather than the interpretative group. It is the music of a submerged people, who *feel* free, and this is precisely how young people feel today. For this reason, the short, violent life of altosaxist Charlie Parker (together with those of Dean and Dylan Thomas) exerts a strong attraction on this generation, because all three went their own uncompromising way, listening to their inner voices, celebrating whatever they could find to celebrate, and then willingly paying the cost in self-destruction. But if young people idolize them, they have no illusions about them as martyrs, for they know (and almost stoically accept) that one of the risks of going so fast, and so far, is death.

But it is perhaps in poetry where the attitude of the Beat Generation, and its exaggerated will to find beliefs at any cost, is most clearly articulated. In San Francisco (which is, in many ways, the Paris of this generation), a whole school of young poets has made a complete break with their elegant, University-imprisoned forebears. Some of them subscribe to Zen Buddhism, which is a highly sophisticated, nonrational psychology of revelation, and wait for satori (wisdom, understanding, reconciliation). Some are Catholic laymen, or even monks, and pray for the redemption of the world. Many of them resemble mendicant friars, or the Goliard balladeers of the Middle Ages, carrying everything they own on their backs, including typewritten copies of their poems to be left, as one of them put it, in art galleries, latrines, 'and other places where poets gather.' All of them believe that only that which cries to be said, no matter how 'unpoetic' it may seem; only that which is unalterably true to the sayer, and bursts out of him in a flood, finding its own form as it comes, is worth the saying in the first place. Literary attitudes, concern about meter or grammar, everything self-conscious and artificial that separates literature from life (they say) has got to go. As a result, their public readings are more like jam sessions than stuffy 'cultural' occasions—with all the attendant shirt sleeves, tenor saxophonists, liquor, and imprecations from the audience. One of them, Allen Ginsberg, whom *Life* Magazine has called the most exciting young poet in America, has written a long, brilliant and disordered poem called *Howl*. It contains a good many expressions and experiences that have never been in a poem before; nevertheless, its aim is so clearly a defense of the human spirit in the face of a civilization intent on destroying it, that the effect is purifying. '*Howl* is an "Affirmation" by individual experience of God, sex, drugs, absurdity,' Ginsberg says.

The same might be said of *On The Road*. Most critics spent so much time expressing their polite distaste for the sordidness of some of the material, that they completely failed to mention that in this world, the world of the Beat Generation, Kerouac unfailingly found tenderness, humility, joy and even reverence; and, though living in what many critics considered a nightmare-jungle of empty sensation, his characters nevertheless could say over and over:

'No one can tell us that there is no God. We've passed through all forms. . . . Everything is fine, God exists, we know time. . . . Furthermore we know America, we're at home. . . . We give and take and go in the incredibly complicated sweetness. . . .'

Whatever else they may be, these are not the words of a generation consumed by self-pity over the loss of their illusions; nor are they the words of a generation consumed by hatred for a world they never made. They seem rather to be the words of a generation groping toward faith out of an intellectual despair and moral chaos in which they refuse to lose themselves. They will strike many people as strange words, coming as they do from the lips of a young man behind the wheel of a fast car, racing through the American night, much as Kerouac's reply to *Nightbeat*'s John Wingate seemed strange, when he was asked to whom he prayed. 'I pray to my little brother, who died, and to my father, and to Buddha, and to Jesus Christ, and to the Virgin Mary,' he said, and then added: 'I pray to those five *people*. . . .'

But if this grouping of a saint, a sage and a savior with two twentieth-century Americans seems strange, it is only because many of us have forgotten (or have never known) how real the spiritual experience can be when all other experiences have failed to satisfy one's hunger. The suggestion, at least in Kerouac's book, is that beyond the violence, the drugs, the jazz, and all the other 'kicks' in which it frantically seeks its identity, this generation will find a faith and become consciously—he believes that it is unconsciously already—a religious generation.

Be that as it may, there are indications that the Beat Generation is not just an American phenomenon. England has its Teddy Boys, Japan its Sun Tribers, and even in Russia there are hipsters of a sort. Everywhere young people are reacting to the growing collectivity of modern life, and the constant threat of collective death, with the same disturbing extremity of individualism. Everywhere they seem to be saying to their elders: 'We are different from you, and we can't believe in the things you believe in—if only because *this* is the world you have wrought.' Everywhere, they are searching for their own answers.

For many of them, the answer may well be jail or madness or death. They may never find the faith that Kerouac believes is at the end of their road. But on one thing they would all agree: the valueless abyss of modern life is unbearable. And if other generations have lamented the fact that theirs was 'the worst of all possible worlds,' young people today seem to know that it is the only one that they will ever have, and that it is *how* a man lives, not why, that makes all the difference. Their assumption—that the foundation of all systems, moral or social, is the indestructible unit of the single individual—may be nothing but a rebellion against a century in which this idea has fallen into disrepute. But their recognition that what sustains the individual is belief—and their growing conviction that only spiritual beliefs have any lasting validity in a world such as ours—should put their often frenzied behavior in a new light, and will certainly figure large in whatever future they may have.

DIANA TRILLING

THE OTHER NIGHT AT COLUMBIA: A REPORT FROM THE ACADEMY

The 'beats' were to read their poetry at Columbia on Thursday evening and on the spur of the moment three wives from the English department had decided to go to hear them. But for me, one of the three, the spur of the moment was not where the story had begun. It had begun much farther back, some twelve or fourteen years ago, when Allen Ginsberg had been a student at Columbia and I had heard about him much more than I usually hear of students for the simple reason that he got into a great deal of trouble which involved his instructors, and had to be rescued and revived and restored; eventually he had even to be kept out of jail. Of course there was always the question, should this young man be rescued, should he be restored? There was even the question, shouldn't he go to jail? We argued about it some at home but the discussion, I'm afraid, was academic, despite my old resistance to the idea that people like Ginsberg had the right to ask and receive preferential treatment just because they read Rimbaud and Gide and undertook to put words on paper themselves. Nor was my principle (if one may call it that) of equal responsibility for poets and shoe clerks so firm that I didn't need to protect it by refusing to confront Ginsberg as an individual or potential acquaintance. I don't mean that I was aware, at the time, of this motive for disappearing on the two or three occasions when he came to the house to deliver a new batch of poems and report on his latest adventures in sensation-seeking. If I'd been asked to explain, then, my wish not to meet and talk with this troublesome young man who had managed to break through the barrier of student anonymity, I suppose I'd have rested with the proposition that I don't like mess, and I'd have been ready to defend myself against the charge, made in the name of art, of a strictness of judgment which was intolerant of this much deviation from respectable standards of behavior.

Ten, twelve, fourteen years ago, there was still something of a challenge in the 'conventional' position; I still enjoyed defending the properties and proprieties of the middle class against friends who persisted in scorning them. Of course, once upon a time—but that was in the '30's—one had had to defend even having a comfortable chair to sit in, or a rug on the floor. But by the '40's things had changed; one's most intransigent literary friends had capitulated by then, everybody had a well-upholstered sofa and I was reduced to such marginal causes as the Metropolitan Museum, after-dinner coffee cups, and the expectation that visitors would go home by 2 a.m. and put their ashes in the ashtrays. Then why should I not also defend the expectation that a student at Columbia, even a poet, would do his work, submit it to his teachers through the normal channels of classroom communication, stay out of jail, and then, if things went right, graduate, start publishing, be reviewed, and see what developed, whether he was a success or failure?

Well, for Ginsberg, things didn't go right for quite a while. The time came when he was graduated from Columbia and published his poems, but first he got into considerable difficulty, beginning with his suspension from college and the requirement that he submit to psychiatric treatment, and terminating—but this was quite a few years later—in an encounter with the police from which he was extricated by some of his old teachers who thought he needed a hospital more than a prison. The suspension had been for a year, when Ginsberg had been a Senior; the situation was not without its grim humor. It seems that Ginsberg had traced an obscenity in the dusty windows of Hartley Hall; the words were too shocking for the Dean of Students to speak, he had written them on a piece of paper which he pushed across the desk: 'F- - - the Jews.' Even the part of Lionel that wanted to laugh couldn't, it was too hard for the Dean to have to transmit this message to a Jewish professor—this was still in the '40's when being a Jew in the university was not yet what it is today. 'But he's a Jew himself,' said the Dean. 'Can you understand his writing a thing like that?' Yes, Lionel could understand; but he couldn't explain it to the Dean. And anyway he knew that the legend in the dust of Hartley Hall required more than an understanding of Jewish self-hatred and also that it was not the sole cause for administrative uneasiness about Ginsberg and his cronies. It was ordinary good sense for the college to take therapeutic measures with Ginsberg.

I now realize that even at this early point in his career I had already accumulated a fund of information about young Ginsberg which accurately forecast his present talent for self-promotion although it was surely disproportionate to the place he commanded in his teacher's mind and quite contradicted the uncertain physical impression I had caught in opening the door to him when he came to the apartment. He was middling tall, slight, dark, sallow; his dress suggested shabby gentility, poor brown tweed gone threadbare and yellow. The description would have fitted any number of undergraduates of his or any Columbia generation; it was the personal story that set him acutely apart. He came from New Jersey where his father was a school teacher, or perhaps a principal, who himself wrote poetry too—I think for the *New York Times*, which would be as good a way as any of defining the separation between father and son. His mother was in a mental institution, and, off and on, she had been there for a long time. This was the central and utterly persuasive fact of this young man's life; I knew this before I was told it in poetry at Columbia the other night, and doubtless it was this knowledge that underlay the nervous irritability with which I responded to so much as the mention of Ginsberg's name. Here was a boy to whom an outrageous injustice had been done: his mother had gone mad on him, and now whoever crossed his path became somehow responsible, guilty, caught in the impossibility of rectifying what she had done. It was an unfair burden to put on those who were only the later accidents of his history and it made me more defensive than charitable with this poor object of her failure. No boy, after all, could ask anyone to help him build a career on the terrible but gratuitous circumstance of a mad mother; it was a justification for neither poetry nor prose nor yet for 'philosophy' of the kind young Ginsberg liked to expound to his teacher.

161

In the question period which followed the poetry-reading the other night at Columbia, this matter of a rationale for the behavior of Ginsberg and his friends came up: someone asked Ginsberg to state his philosophy. It was a moment I had been awaiting and I thought: 'Here we go; he'll tell us how he's crazy like a daisy and how his friend Orlovsky is crazy like a butterfly.' I had been reading *Time* magazine; who hadn't? But, instead, Ginsberg answered that he had no philosophy; he spoke of inspiration, or perhaps it was illumination, ecstatic illumination, as the source of his poetry and I was more than surprised, I was curiously pleased for him because I took it as a considerable advance in self-control that he could operate with this much shrewdness and leave it, at least for this occasion, to his audience to abstract a 'position' from his and his friends' antics while he himself moved wild, mild, and innocent through the jungle of speculation. Back in the older days, it had always been my feeling that so far as his relationship with his teacher was concerned, this trying to formulate a philosophy must reveal its falseness even to himself, so that his recourse to it insulted his intelligence. Two motives, it seemed to me, impelled him then: the wish to shock his teacher, and the wish to meet the teacher on equal ground. The first of these motives was complicated enough, involving as it did the gratifications of self-incrimination and disapproval, and then forgiveness; but the second was more tangled still. To talk with one's English professor who was also a writer, a critic, and one who made no bones about his solid connection with literary tradition, about one's descent from Rimbaud, Baudelaire or Dostoevsky was clearly to demonstrate a good-sized rationality and order in what was apparently an otherwise undisciplined life. Even more, or so I fancied, it was to propose an alliance between the views of the academic and the poet-rebel, the unity of a deep discriminating commitment to literature which must certainly one day wipe out the fortuitous distance between boy and man, pupil and teacher. Thus, Ginsberg standing on the platform at Columbia and refusing the philosophy gambit might well be taken as an impulse toward manhood, or at least manliness, for which one might be grateful.

But I remind myself: Ginsberg at Columbia on Thursday night was not Ginsberg at Chicago—according to *Time*, at any rate—or Ginsberg at Hunter either, where Kerouac ran the show and a dismal show it must have been, with Kerouac drinking on the platform and clapping James Wechsler's hat on his head in a grand parade of contempt—they were two of four panelists gathered to discuss, 'Is there such a thing as a beat generation?'—and leading Ginsberg out from the wings like a circus donkey. For whatever reason—rumor had it he was in a personal crisis—Kerouac didn't appear on Thursday night, and Ginsberg at Columbia was Ginsberg his own man, dealing with his own history, and intent, it seemed to me, on showing up the past for the poor inaccurate thing it so often is: it's a chance we all dream of but mostly it works the other way around, like the long-ago story of Jed Harris coming back to Yale and sitting on the fence weeping for a youth he could never re-write no matter how many plays of Chekhov he brought to Broadway, no matter how much money he made. I suppose I have no right to say now, and on such early and little evidence, that Ginsberg had always desperately wanted to be respectable, or respected, like his instructors at Columbia, it is so likely that this is a hindsight which suits my needs. It struck me, though, that this was the most unmistakable and touching message from platform to audience the other night, and as I received it, I felt I had known something like it all along. Not that Ginsberg had ever shown himself as a potential future colleague in the university; anything but that. Even the implied literary comradeship had had reference, not to any possibility of Ginsberg's assimilation into the community of professors, but to the professor's capacity for association in the community of rebellious young poets. Still, it was not just anyone on the campus to whom Ginsberg had come with his lurid boasts which were also his confession; it was Lionel, it was Mark Van Doren; if there was anyone else he would very likely be of the same respectable species, and I remember saying, 'He wants you to forbid him to behave like that. He wants you to take him out of it, else why does he choose people like you and Mark to tell these stories to?' To which I received always the same answer, 'I'm not his father,' with which there could of course be no argument.

And yet, even granting the accuracy of this reconstruction of the past, it would be wrong to conclude that any consideration of motive on Ginsberg's part was sufficiently strong to alter one's first and most forceful image of Ginsberg as a 'case'—a gifted and sad case, a guilt-provoking and nuisance case but, above all, a case. Nor was it a help that Lionel had recently published a story about a crazy student and a supposedly normal student in which the author's affection was so plainly directed to the former; we never became used to the calls, often in the middle of the night, asking whether it wasn't the crazy character who was really sane. Ginsberg, with his poems in which there was never quite enough talent or hard work, and with his ambiguous need to tell his teacher exactly what new flagrancy he was now exploring with his Gide-talking friends at the West End Café had at any rate the distinction of being more crudely justified in his emotional disturbance than most; he also had the distinction of carrying mental unbalance in the direction of criminality, a territory one preferred to leave unclaimed by student or friend.

Gide and the West End Café in all its upper-Broadway dreariness: what could the two conceivably have in common except those lost boys of the '40's? How different it might have been for Ginsberg and his friends if they had come of age ten or fifteen years sooner was one of the particular sadnesses of the other evening, it virtually stood on the platform with them as the poets read their poems whose chief virtue, it seemed to me, was their 'racial-minority' funniness, their 'depressed-classes' funniness of a kind which has never had so sure and live a place as it did in the '30's, the embittered fond funniness which has to do with one's own awful family, funniness plain and poetical, always aware of itself, of a kind which would seem now to have all but disappeared among intellectuals except as an eclecticism or a device of self-pity. It's a real loss; I hadn't quite realized how much I missed it until Thursday night when Ginsberg read his poem, 'The Ignu,' and Corso read his poem, 'Marriage' (a compulsive poem, he called it, about a compulsive subject) and they were still funny in that old racial depressed way but not nearly as funny and authentic as they would have been had they been written before the Jews and the Italians and the Negroes, but especially the Jews, had been crammed down their own and everyone else's throat as Americans-like-everyone-else instead of outsiders raised in the Bronx or on Ninth Avenue or even in Georgia. The Jew in particular is a loss to literature and life—I mean the Jew out of which was bred the Jewish intellectual of the '30's. For a few short years in the '30's, as not before or since, the Jew was at his funniest, wisest best; he perfectly well knew the advantage he could count on in the Gentile world, and that there was no ascendancy or pride the Gentile comrades could muster against a roomful of Jewish sympathizers singing at the tops of their voices, 'A SOCialist union is a NO good union, is a COMpan-y union of the bosses,' or against Michael Gold's mother who wanted to know did her boy have to write books the whole world should know she had bedbugs. If Ginsberg had been born in an earlier generation it would surely have been the Stewart Cafeteria in the Village that he and his friends would have hung out at instead of the West End, that dim waystation of undergraduate debauchery on Morningside Heights—and the Stewart Cafeteria was a well-lighted place and one of the funniest places in New York; at least, at every other table it was funny, and where it was decadent or even conspiratorial, this had its humor too, or at least its robustness. As for Gide—the Gide of the '30's was the 'betrayer of the Revolution,' not the Gide of the *acte gratuite* and homosexuality in North Africa. One didn't use pathology in those days to explain or excuse or exhibit oneself and one never had to be lonely; there was never a less lonely time for intellectuals than the Depression, or a less depressed time—unless, of course, one was recalcitrant, like Fitzgerald, and simply refused to be radicalized, in which stubborn case it couldn't have been lonelier. Intellectuals talk now about how, in the '30's, there was an 'idea' in life, not the emptiness we live in. Actually, it

165

was a time of generally weak intellection—so many of us who put our faith in Marx and Lenin had read neither of them—but of very strong feeling. Everyone judged everyone else, it was a time of incessant cruel moral judgment; today's friend was tomorrow's enemy; whoever disagreed with oneself had sold out, God knows to or for what, maybe for $10 more a week; there was little of the generosity among intellectuals which nowadays dictates the automatic, 'Gee, that's great' at any news of someone else's good fortune. But it was surely a time of quicker, truer feeling than is now conjured up with marijuana or the infantile camaraderie of *On The Road*. And there was paradox but no contradiction in this double truth, just as there was no contradiction in the fact that it was a time in which the neurotic determination of the intellectual was being so universally acted out and yet a time in which, whatever his dedication to historical or economic determinism, personally he had a unique sense of free will. In the '30's one's clinical vocabulary was limited to two words—escapism and subjectivism—and both of them applied only to other people's wrong political choices.

Well, the 'beats' weren't lucky enough to be born except when they were born. Ginsberg says he lives in Harlem, but it's not the Harlem of the Scottsboro boys and W. C. Handy and the benign insanity of trying to proletarianize Striver's Row; their comrades are not the comrades of the Stewart Cafeteria nor yet of the road, as Kerouac would disingenuously have it, but pick-ups on dark morning streets. But they have their connection with us who were young in the '30's, their intimate political connection, which we deny at risk of missing what it is that makes the 'beat' phenomenon something to think about. As they used to say on 14th Street, it is no accident, comrades, it is decidedly no accident that today in the '50's our single overt manifestation of protest takes the wholly non-political form of a bunch of panic-stricken kids in blue jeans, many of them publicly homosexual, talking about or taking drugs, assuring us that they are out of their minds, not responsible, while the liberal intellectual is convinced that he has no power to control the political future, the future of the free world, and that therefore he must submit to what he defines as political necessity. Though of course the various aspects of a culture must be granted their own autonomous source and character, the connection between 'beat' and respectable liberal intellectual exists and is not hard to locate: the common need to deny free will, divest oneself of responsibility and yet stay alive. The typical liberal intellectual of the '50's, whether he be a writer for *Partisan Review* or a law school professor or a magazine or newspaper editor, explains his evolution over the last two decades—specifically, his present attitude toward 'co-existence'—by telling us that he has been forced to accept the unhappy reality of Soviet strength in an atomic world, and that there is no alternative to capitulation—not that he calls it that—except the extinction of nuclear war. Even the diplomacy he invokes is not so much flexible, which he would like to think it is, as disarmed and, hopefully, disarming, an instrument of his impulse to surrender rather than of any wish to dominate or even of his professed wish to hold the line. Similarly docile to culture, the 'beat' also contrives a fate by predicating a fate. Like the respectable established intellectual—or the organization man, or the suburban matron—against whom he makes his play of protest, he conceives of himself as incapable of exerting any substantive influence against the forces that condition him. He is made by society, he cannot make society. He can only stay alive as best he can for as long as is permitted him. Is it any wonder, then, that *Time* and *Life* write as they do about the 'beats'—with such a conspicuous show of superiority, and no hint of fear? These periodicals know what genuine, dangerous protest looks like, and it doesn't look like Ginsberg and Kerouac. Clearly, there is no more menace in *Howl* or *On The Road* than there is in the Scarsdale PTA. In the common assumption of effectlessness, in the apparent will to rest with a social determination over which the individual spirit and intelligence cannot and perhaps even should not try to triumph, there may emerge any number of the disparate elements of our present culture—from the liberal intellectual journals to Luce to the Harvard Law School, from Ginsberg to the suburban matron.

But then why, one ponders, do one's most relaxed and non-square friends, alongside of whom one can oneself be made to look like the original object with four sides of equal length; why do one's most politically 'flexible' friends, alongside of whom one's own divergence from dominant liberal opinion is regularly made to look so ungraceful, so like a latter-day sectarianism, even a fanaticism, feel constrained to dispute Columbia's judgment in giving the 'beats' a hearing on the campus and my own wish to attend their poetry-reading? Why, for instance, the dissent of Dwight MacDonald, whom I happened to see that afternoon; or of W. H. Auden, who, when I said I had been moved by the performance, gently chided me, 'I'm ashamed of you'; or of William Phillips who, although he tells me yes, I may go ahead with this article, can't hide his puzzlement, even worry, because I want to give the 'beats' this kind of attention? In strict logic, it would seem to me that things should go in quite the other direction and that I, who insist upon at least the assumption of free will in our political dealings with Russia, who insist upon what I call political responsibility, should be the one to protest a university forum for the irresponsibles whereas my friends whose politics are what I think of as finally a politics of victimization, of passivity and fatedness, should be able to shrug off the 'beats' as merely another inevitable, if tasteless, expression of a *Zeitgeist* with which I believe them to be far more in tune than I am. I do not mean, of course, to rule out taste, or style, as a valid criterion of moral judgment. A sense of social overwhelmment which announces itself in terms of disreputableness or even criminality asks for a different kind of moral assessment than the same emotion kept within the bounds of acceptable social expression. But I would simply point to the similarities which are masked by these genuine moral differences between the 'beats' and my friends who would caution us against them. Taste or style dictates that most intellectuals behave decorously, earn a regular living, disguise instead of flaunt whatever may be their private digressions from the conduct society considers desirable; when they seek support for the poetical impulse or ask for light on their self-doubt and fears, they don't make the naked boast that they are crazy like daisies but they elaborate a new belief in the indispensability of neurosis to art, or beat the bushes for some new deviant psychoanalysis which will generalize their despair without curing it. And these differences of style are of course important, at least for the moment. It is from the long-range, and no doubt absolute, view of our immediate cultural situation, which bears so closely upon our continuing national crisis, that the moral difference between a respectable and a disreputable acceptance of defeat seems to me to constitute little more than a cultural footnote to history.

But perhaps I wander too far from the other night at Columbia. There was enough in the evening that was humanly immediate to divert one from this kind of ultimate concern. . . .

It was not an official university occasion. The 'beats' appeared at Columbia on the invitation of a student club—interestingly enough, the John Dewey Society. Whether the club first approached Ginsberg or Ginsberg initiated the proceedings, I don't know, but what had happened was that Ginsberg in his undergraduate days had taken a loan from the university—$200? $250?—and recently the Bursar's office had caught up with him in his new incarnation of successful literary itinerant, to demand repayment. Nothing if not ingenious, Ginsberg now proposed to pay off his debt by reading his poetry at Columbia without fee. It was at this point that various members of the English department, solicited as sponsors for the operation, had announced their rejection of the whole deal, literary as well as financial, and the performance was arranged without financial benefit to Ginsberg and without official cover; we three wives, however, decided to attend on our own. We would meet at 7:45 at the door of the theater; no, we would meet at 7:40 at the door of the theater; no, we would meet no later than 7:30 across the street from the theater: the telephoning back and forth among the three women was stupendous as word spread of vast barbarian hordes converging on poor dull McMillin Theater from all the dark recesses of the city, howling for their leader. The advance warnings turned out to be exaggerated; it was nevertheless disconcerting to be associated with such goings-on, and the fact that Fred Dupee, at the request of the John Dewey Society, had consented to be moderator, chairman, introducer of Ginsberg and his fellow-poets, while it provided the wives of his colleagues with the assurance of seats in a section of the hall reserved for faculty, was not without its uncomfortable reminder that Ginsberg had, in a sense, got his way; he was appearing on the same Columbia platform from which T. S. Eliot had last year read his poetry; he was being presented by, and was thus bound to be thought under the sponsorship of, an important person in the academic and literary community who was also one's long-time friend. And indeed it was as Dupee's friend that one took a first canvass of the scene: the line of policemen before the entrance to the theater; the air of suppressed excitement in the lobbies and one's own rather contemptible self-consciousness about being seen in such a crowd; the shoddiness of an audience in which it was virtually impossible to distinguish between student and camp-follower; the always-new shock of so many young girls, so few of them pretty, and so many dreadful black stockings; so many young men, so few of them—despite the many black beards—with any promise of masculinity. It was distressing to think that Dupee was going to be 'faculty' to this rabble, that at this moment he was backstage with Ginsberg & Co., formulating a deportment which would check the excess of which one knew them to be capable, even or especially in public, without doing violence to his own large tolerance.

For me, it was of some note that the auditorium smelled fresh. The place was already full when we arrived; I took one look at the crowd and was certain that it would smell bad. But I was mistaken. These people may think they're dirty inside and dress up to it. Nevertheless, they smell all right. The audience was clean and Ginsberg was clean and Corso was clean and Orlovsky was clean. Maybe Ginsberg says he doesn't bathe or shave; Corso, I know, declares that he has never combed his hair; Orlovsky has a line in one of the two poems he read—he's not yet written his third, the chairman explained—'If I should shave, I know the bugs would go away.' But for this occasion, at any rate, Ginsberg, Corso and Orlovsky were all clean and shaven; Kerouac, in crisis, didn't appear, but if he had come he would have been clean and shaven too—he was at Hunter, I've inquired about that. And anyway, there's nothing dirty about a checked shirt or a lumberjacket and blue jeans, they're standard uniform in the best nursery schools. Ginsberg has his pride, as do his friends.

And how do I look to the 'beats,' I ask myself after that experience with the seats, and not only I but the other wives I was with? We had pulled aside the tattered old velvet rope which marked off the section held for faculty, actually it was trailing on the floor, and moved into the seats Dupee's wife Andy had saved for us by strewing coats on them; there was a big grey overcoat she couldn't identify: she stood holding it up in the air murmuring wistfully, 'Whose is this?'—until the young people in the row in back of us took account of us and answered sternly, '*Those* seats are reserved for faculty.' If I have trouble unraveling undergraduates from 'beats,' neither do the wives of the Columbia English department wear their distinction with any certainty.

But Dupee's distinction, that's something else again: what could I have been worrying about, when had Dupee ever failed to meet the occasion, or missed a right style? I don't suppose one could witness a better performance than his on Thursday evening; its rightness was apparent the moment he walked onto the stage, his troupe in tow and himself just close enough and just enough removed to indicate the balance in which he held the situation. Had there been a hint of betrayal in his deportment, of either himself or his guests—naturally, he had made them his guests—the whole evening might have been different: for instance, a few minutes later when the overflow attendance outside the door began to bang and shout for admission, might not the audience have caught the contagion and become unruly too? Or would Ginsberg have stayed with his picture of himself as poet serious and triumphant instead of succumbing to what must have been the greatest temptation to spoil his opportunity? 'The last time I was in this theater,' Dupee began quietly, 'it was also to hear a poet read his works. That was T. S. Eliot.' A slight alteration of inflection, from irony to mockery, from condescension to contempt, and it might well have been a signal for near-riot, boos and catcalls and whistlings; the evening would have been lost to the 'beats,' Dupee and Columbia would have been defeated. Dupee transformed a circus into a classroom. He himself, he said, welcomed the chance to hear these poets read their works—he never once in his remarks gave them their name of 'beats' nor alluded even to San Francisco—because in all poetry it was important to study the spoken accent; he himself didn't happen especially to admire those of their works that he knew; still, he would draw our attention to their skillful use of a certain kind of American imagery which, deriving from Whitman, yet passed Whitman's use of it or even Hart Crane's. . . . It was Dupee speaking for the Academy, claiming for it its place in life, and the performers were inevitably captive to his dignity and self-assurance. Rather than Ginsberg and his friends, it was a photographer from *Life*, exploding his flashbulbs in everybody's face, mounting a ladder at the back of the stage the more effectively to shoot his angles, who came to represent vulgarity and disruption and disrespect; when a student in the audience disconnected a wire which had something to do with the picture-taking, one guessed that Ginsberg was none too happy but it was the photographer's face that became ugly, the only real ugliness of the evening. One could feel nothing but pity for Ginsberg and his friends that their front of disreputableness and rebellion should be this transparent, this vulnerable to the seductions of a clever host. With Dupee's introduction, the whole of their defense had been penetrated at the very outset.

Pity is not the easiest of our emotions today; now it's understanding that is easy, and more and more—or so I find it for myself—real pity moves hand-in-hand with real terror; it's an emotion one avoids because it's so hard; one understands the cripple, the delinquent, the unhappy so as not to have to pity them. But Thursday night was an occasion of pity so direct and inescapable that it left little to the understanding that wasn't mere afterthought—and pity not only for the observed, the performers, but for us who had come to observe them and reassure ourselves that we were not implicated. One might as readily persuade oneself one was not implicated in one's children! For this was it: these *were* children, miserable children trying desperately to manage, asking desperately to be taken out of it all; there was nothing one could imagine except to bundle them home and feed them warm milk, promise them they need no longer call for mama and papa. I kept asking myself, where had I had just such an experience before, and later it came to me: I had gone to see O'Neill's *Long Day's Journey into Night* and the play had echoed with just such a child's cry for help; at intermission time all the mothers in the audience were so tormented and anxious that they rushed in a body to phone home: was the baby really all right, was he really well and warm in his bed; one couldn't get near the telephone booths. A dozen years ago, when Ginsberg had been a student and I had taxed Lionel with the duty to forbid him to misbehave, he had answered me that he wasn't the boy's father, and of course he was right. Neither was Mark Van Doren the boy's father; a teacher is not a father to his students and he must never try to be. Besides, Ginsberg had a father of his own who couldn't be replaced at will: he was in the audience the other night. One of the things Ginsberg read was part of a long poem to his mother who, he told us, had died three years ago, and as he read it, he choked and cried; but no one in the audience tittered or showed embarrassment at this public display of emotion, and I doubt whether anyone thought, 'See, he has existence: he can cry, he can feel.' Nor did anyone seem very curious when he went on to explain, later in the evening, that the reason he had cried was because his father was in the theater. I have no way of knowing what Ginsberg's father felt the other night about his son being up there on the stage at Columbia (it rather obsesses me), but I should guess he was proud; it's what I'd conclude from his expression at the end of the performance when Ginsberg beat through the admirers who surrounded him, to get to his father as quickly as he could: surely that's nice for a father. And I should suppose a father was bound to be pleased that his son was reading his poems in a university auditorium: it would

mean the boy's success, and this would be better than a
vulgarity, it would necessarily include the chairman's critical
gravity and the fact, however bizarre, that T. S. Eliot had been
the last poet in this place before him. In a sense, Orlovsky and
Corso were more orphans than Ginsberg the other night, but
this was not necessarily because they were without fathers of
their own in the audience; I should think it would go back
much farther than this, to whatever it was that made them
look so much more armored, less openly eager for approval;
although they were essentially as innocent and childlike as
Ginsberg, they couldn't begin to match his appeal; it was on
Ginsberg that one's eye rested, it was to the sweetness in his
face and to his sweet smile that one responded; it was to him
that one gave one's pity and for him one felt one's own fullest
terror. Clearly, I am no judge of his poem, 'Lion in the Room,'
which he announced was dedicated to Lionel Trilling; I heard
it through too much sympathy, and also self-consciousness.
The poem was addressed as well as dedicated to Lionel; it was
about a lion in the room with the poet, a lion who was hungry
but refused to eat him; I heard it as a passionate love-poem, I
really can't say whether it was a good or bad poem, but I was
much moved by it, in some part unaccountably. It was also a
decent poem, it now strikes me; I mean, there were no obscenities in it as there had been in much of the poetry the 'beats'
read. Here was something else that was remarkable about the
other evening: most of the audience was very young, and
Ginsberg must have realized this because when he read the
poem about his mother and came to the place where he
referred to the YPSLs of her girlhood, he interposed his only
textual exegesis of the evening: in an aside he explained,
'Young People's Socialist League'—he was very earnest about
wanting his poetry to be understood. And it wasn't only his
gentility that distinguished Ginsberg's father from the rest of
the audience; as far as I could see, he was the only man in the
hall who looked old enough to be the father of a grown son;
the audience was crazily young, there were virtually no faculty
present, I suppose they didn't want to give this much sanction
to the 'beats.' For this young audience the obscenities read

from the stage seemed to have no force whatsoever; there was not even the shock of silence, and when Ginsberg forgot himself in the question period and said that something or other was bull-shit, I think he was more upset than his listeners; I can't imagine anything more detached and scientific outside a psychoanalyst's office, or perhaps a nursery school, than this young audience at Columbia. Of Corso, in particular, one had the sense that he mouthed the bad word only with considerable personal difficulty: this hurts me more than it hurts you.

Obviously, the whole performance had been carefully devised as to who would read first and what, then who next, and just how much an audience could take without becoming bored and over-critical: it would be my opinion we could have taken a bit more before the question period which must have been an anti-climax for anyone who had come, not as a tourist, but as a fellow-traveller. I've already reported how Ginsberg dealt with the philosophy question. There remains, of the question period, only to report his views on verse forms.

I don't remember how the question was put to Ginsberg—but I'm sure it was put neutrally: no one was inclined to embarrass the guests—which led him into a discussion of prosody; perhaps it was the question about what Ginsberg as a poet had learned at Columbia; but anyway, here, at last, Ginsberg had a real classroom subject: he could be a teacher who wed outrageousness to authority in the time-honored way of the young and lively, no-pedant-he performer of the classroom, and suddenly Ginsberg heard himself announcing that no one at Columbia knew anything about prosody; the English department was stuck in the nineteenth century, sensible of no meter other than the old iambic pentameter, whereas the thing about him and his friends was their concern with a poetic line which moved in the rhythm of ordinary speech; they were poetic innovators, carrying things forward the logical next step from William Carlos Williams. And now all at once the thing about Ginsberg and his friends was not their social protest and existentialism, their whackiness and beat-upness: suddenly it had become their energy of poetic impulse that earned them their right to be heard in the university, their studious devotion to their art: Ginsberg was seeing to that. Orlovsky had made his contribution to the evening; he had read his two whacky uproarious poems, the entire canon of his work, and had won his acclaim. Corso had similarly given his best, and been approved. The question period, the period of instruction, belonged to Ginsberg alone, and his friends might be slightly puzzled by the turn the evening had taken, the decorousness of which they suddenly found themselves a part—Corso, for instance, began to look like a chastened small boy who was still determined, though his heart was no longer in it, to bully his way through against all these damned grown-ups—but they had no choice except to permit their companion his deviation into high-mindedness. (Rightest opportunism?) Thus did one measure, finally, the full tug of something close to respectability in Ginsberg's life, by this division in the ranks; and thus, too, was the soundness of Dupee's reminder, that there is always something to learn from hearing a poet read his poems aloud, borne in on one. For the fact was that Ginsberg, reading his verse, had naturally given it the iambic beat: after all, it is the traditional beat of English poetry where it deals with serious subjects as Ginsberg's poems so often do. A poet, one thought—and it was a poignant thought because it came so immediately and humanly rather than as an abstraction—may choose to walk whatever zany path in his life as a man; but when it comes to mourning and mothers and such, he will be drawn into the line of tradition; at least in this far he has a hard time avoiding respectability.

The evening was over, we were dismissed to return to our homes. A crowd formed around Ginsberg; he extricated himself and came to his father a few rows ahead of us. I resisted the temptation to overhear their greeting. In some part of me I wanted to speak to Ginsberg, tell him I had liked the poem he had written to my husband, but I didn't do it: I couldn't be sure that Ginsberg wouldn't take my meaning wrong; after all, his social behavior is not fantasy. Outside, it had blown up a bit—or was it just the chill of unreality against which we hurried to find shelter?

There was a meeting going on at home of the pleasant

professional sort which, like the comfortable living-room in which it usually takes place, at a certain point in a successful modern literary career confirms the writer in his sense of disciplined achievement and well-earned reward. I had found myself hurrying as if I were needed, but there was really no reason for my haste; my entrance was an interruption, even a disturbance of the attractive scene. Auden, alone of the eight men in the room not dressed in a proper suit but wearing his battered old brown leather jacket, was first to inquire about my experience. I told him I had been moved; he answered that he was ashamed of me. I said, 'It's different when it's a sociological phenomenon and when it's human beings,' and he of course knew and accepted what I said. Yet as I prepared to get out of the room so that the men could sit down again with their drinks, I felt there was something more I had to add—it was not enough to leave the 'beats' only as human beings—and so I said, 'Allen Ginsberg read a love-poem to you, Lionel. I liked it very much.' It was a strange thing to say in the circumstances, perhaps even a little foolish. But I'm sure that Ginsberg's old teacher knew what I was saying, and why I was impelled to say it.

ALLEN GINSBERG

FROM *PARIS REVIEW* INTERVIEW (1965)

INTERVIEWER: Has there been a time when fear of censorship or similar trouble has made your own expression difficult?

GINSBERG: This is so complicated a matter. The beginning of the fear with me was, you know, what would my father say to something that I would write. At the time, writing 'Howl'—for instance, like I assumed when writing it that it was something that *could* not be published because I wouldn't want my daddy to see what was in there. About my sex life, being fucked in the ass, imagine your father reading a thing like that, was what I thought. Though that disappeared as soon as the thing was real, or as soon as I manifested my . . . you know, it didn't make that much importance finally. That was sort of a help for writing, because I assumed that it wouldn't be published, therefore I could say anything that I wanted. So literally just for myself or anybody that I knew personally well, writers who would be willing to appreciate it with a breadth of tolerance—in a piece of work like 'Howl'—who wouldn't be judging from a moralistic viewpoint but looking for evidences of humanity or secret thought or just actual truthfulness.

Then there's later the problem of publication—we had a lot. The English printer refused at first I think, we were afraid of customs; the first edition we had to print with asterisks on some of the dirty words, and then the *Evergreen Review* in reprinting it used asterisks, and various people reprinting it later always wanted to use the *Evergreen* version rather than the corrected legal City Lights version—like I think there's an anthology of Jewish writers, I forgot who edited that, but a couple of the high-class intellectuals from Columbia. I had written asking them specifically to use the later City Lights version, but they went ahead and printed an asterisked version. I forget what was the name of that—something like *New Generation of Jewish Writing*, Philip Roth, et cetera.

INTERVIEWER: Do you take difficulties like these as social

problems, problems of communication simply, or do you feel they also block your own ability to express yourself for yourself?

GINSBERG: The problem is, where it gets to literature, is this. We all talk among ourselves and we have common understandings, and we say anything we want to say, and we talk about our assholes, and we talk about our cocks, and we talk about who we fucked last night, or who we're gonna fuck tomorrow, or what kind love affair we have, or when we got drunk, or when we stuck a broom in our ass in the Hotel Ambassador in Prague—anybody tells one's friends about that. So then—what happens if you make a distinction between what you tell your friends and what you tell your Muse? The problem is to break down that distinction: when you approach the Muse to talk as frankly as you would talk with yourself or with your friends. So I began finding, in conversations with Burroughs and Kerouac and Gregory Corso, in conversations with people whom I knew well, whose souls I respected, that the things we were telling each other for real were totally different from what was already in literature. And that was Kerouac's great discovery in *On the Road*. The kinds of things that he and Neal Cassady were talking about, he finally discovered were *the* subject matter for what he wanted to write down. That meant, at that minute, a complete revision of what literature was supposed to be, in *his* mind, and actually in the minds of the people that first read the book. Certainly in the minds of the critics, who had at first attacked it as not being . . . proper structure, or something. In other words, a gang of friends running around in an automobile. Which obviously is like a great picaresque literary device, and a classical one. And was *not* recognized, at the time, as suitable literary subject matter.

INTERVIEWER: So it's not just a matter of themes—sex, or any other one—

GINSBERG: It's the ability to commit to writing, to *write*, the same way that you . . . are! Anyway! You have many writers who have preconceived ideas about what literature is supposed to be, and their ideas seem to exclude that which makes them most charming in private conversation. Their faggishness, or their campiness, or their neurasthenia, or their solitude, or their goofiness, or their—even—masculinity, at times. Because they think that they're gonna write something that sounds like something else that they've read before, instead of sounds like them. Or comes from their own life. In other words, there's no distinction, there should be no distinction between what we write down, and what we really know, to begin with. As we know it every day, with each other. And the hypocrisy of literature has been—you know like there's supposed to be formal literature, which is supposed to be different from . . . in subject, in diction, and even in organization, from our quotidian inspired lives.

It's also like in Whitman, 'I find no fat sweeter than that which sticks to my own bones'—that is to say the self-confidence of someone who knows that he's really alive, and that his existence is just as good as any other subject matter.

INTERVIEWER: Is physiology a part of this too—like the difference between your long breath line, and William Carlos Williams's shorter unit?

GINSBERG: Analytically, ex post facto, it all begins with fucking around and intuition and without any idea of *what* you're doing, I think. Later, I have a tendency to explain it, 'Well, I got a longer breath than Williams, or I'm Jewish, or I study yoga, or I sing long lines. . . .' But anyway, what it boils down to is this, it's my *movement*, my feeling is for a big long clanky statement—partly that's something that I share, or maybe that I even got from Kerouac's long prose line; which is really, like he once remarked, an extended poem. Like one long sentence page of his in *Doctor Sax* or *Railroad Earth* or occasionally *On the Road*—if you examine them phrase by phrase they usually have the density of poetry, and the beauty of poetry, but most of all the single elastic rhythm running from beginning to end of the line and ending 'mop!'

INTERVIEWER: Have you ever wanted to extend this rhythmic feeling as far as, say, Artaud or now Michael McClure have taken it—to a line that is actually animal noise?

GINSBERG: The rhythm of the long line is also an animal cry.

INTERVIEWER: So you're following that feeling and not a thought or a visual image?

GINSBERG: It's simultaneous. The poetry generally is like a rhythmic articulation of feeling. The feeling is like an impulse that rises within—just like sexual impulses, say; it's almost as definite as that. It's a feeling that begins somewhere in the pit of the stomach and rises up forward in the breast and then comes out through the mouth and ears, and comes forth a croon or a groan or a sigh. Which, if you put words to it by looking around and seeing and trying to describe what's making you sigh—and sigh in words—you simply articulate what you're feeling. As simple as that. Or actually what happens is, at best what happens, is there's a definite body rhythm that has no definite words, or may have one or two words attached to it, one or two key words attached to it. And then, in writing it down, it's simply by a process of association that I find what the rest of the statement is—what can be collected around that word, what that word is connected to. Partly by simple association, the first thing that comes to my mind like 'Moloch is' or 'Moloch who,' and then whatever comes out. But that also goes along with a definite rhythmic impulse, like DA de de DA de de DA de de DA DA. 'Moloch whose eyes are a thousand blind windows.' And before I wrote 'Moloch whose eyes are a thousand blind windows,' I had the word, 'Moloch, Moloch, Moloch,' and I also had the feeling DA de de DA de de DA de de DA DA. So it was just a question of looking up and seeing a lot of windows, and saying, Oh, windows, of course, but what kind of windows? But not even that—'Moloch whose eyes.' 'Moloch whose eyes'—which is beautiful in itself—but what about it, Moloch whose eyes are what? So Moloch whose eyes—then probably the next thing I thought was 'thousands.' O.K., and then thousands what? 'Thousands blind.' And I had to finish it somehow. So I hadda say 'windows.' It looked good afterward.

Usually during the composition, step by step, word by word and adjective by adjective, if it's at all spontaneous, I don't know whether it even makes sense sometimes. Sometimes I do know it makes complete sense, and I start crying. Because I realize I'm hitting some area which is absolutely true. And in that sense applicable universally, or understandable universally. In that sense able to survive through time—in that sense to be read by somebody and wept to, maybe, centuries later. In that sense prophecy, because it touches a common key . . . what prophecy actually is is not that you actually know that the bomb will fall in 1942. It's that you know and feel something which somebody knows and feels in a hundred years. And maybe articulate it in a hint—concrete way that they can pick up on in a hundred years.

ALLEN GINSBERG

KEROUAC*

AG: Most prose writers aren't even aware that the sentence they write has a sound, are not even concerned with sound in prose. In fact I'm not sure what most of them are concerned with. Most prose writers that I grew up with in college were influenced a lot by Hemingway, so one of their main concerns was economy in writing down the facts in journalisticese subjectivity—that is, economy in writing down little insights and perceptions as to how white the dawn was or how cold the icy water was, with the idea in mind of getting a surprising, fresh little short-sentenced, maybe haiku-like image out of it, or at least being accurate as a newspaper—the prose should be as well-written as newspaper prose, at least, in giving the facts—but rarely with the knowledge that it was a sentence which could be spoken aloud, and rarely with the knowledge that it was a sentence which should be in total vernacular spoken aloud, and also rarely with the knowledge that total vernacular spoken aloud has a sound quality. . . . In addition to being pictorial prose, it is also an object of pure sound, and a construction of pure sound, like a mantra, or like with Milton:

> . . . Him the Almighty Power
> Hurl'd headlong flaming from th' Ethereal Sky
> With hideous ruin and combustion down
> To bottomless perdition, there to dwell
> In Adamantine Chains and penal Fire,
> Who durst defy th' Omnipotent to arms.

Kerouac was a regular style prose writer writing in the forms of Thomas Wolfe; that is to say, long, symphonic-sentenced, heavy-voweled periods, a little with echo of Milton. Wolfe had that same Biblical Miltonic prose echo in his sentences, and

*Text of a Fiction Class at Kent State, 6 April 1971.

183

in a book called *The Town and the City* written in the late forties by Kerouac there are similar lengthily constructed sentences.

So Kerouac was the first writer I ever met who heard his own writing, who listened to his own sentences as if they were musical, rhythmical constructions, and who could follow the sequence of sentences that make up the paragraph as if he were listening to a little jazz riff, a complete chorus, say of 'Lady Be Good,' by the then-hero of saxophone, Lester Young, or a later hero of alto, Charlie Parker. So he found a rhythmic model, listening to their rhythms, the rhythm of Lester Young's saxophone sentences or paragraphs in his choruses of 'Lester Leaps In' or any one of a number of—at that time—celebrated jazz classic records (which are still very listenable, if anybody has the historic ear to know them).

And he would model sentences on the choruses, on the particular squiggly little 'dadadadadadaduhdada'—'As I was goin' walkin' down to Larimer' of 'Lester Leaps In' is 'dadada dadadada dadada, dadadadadadada dadada, dadadadada dada dadada, dadaadadaydyadadda.' So it was a definite rhythmical squiggle that he was hearing when he was writing his prose sentences, a funny body rhythm, a breathing rhythm and a speech rhythm that he was conscious of writing when he was writing prose. So he added a dimension to prose which most prosateurs have not yet actually discovered exists or is necessary for epic or historical prose.

Kerouac got to be a great poet on that basis, 'cause he could hear American speech, and he could hear it in musical sequence. He has a book called *Mexico City Blues*—poem choruses, one page apiece, on Buddhist themes, generally, like a little subject rolling from one chorus to the next, one page to another and he would get to funny little rhythmic constructions like

> The Eagle on the Pass,
>   the Wire on the Rail,
>   the High Hot Iron
>   of my heart,

> The Blazing Chickaball
> Whap-by
> Extry special Super
> High Job
> Ole 169 be
> floundering
> Down to Kill Roy

Kill Roy (Gilroy, California) being the end of the Southern Pacific line, where the Southern Pacific finishes in the South. 'The Blazing Chickaball/Whap-by/Extry special Super/High Job/Ole 169 be/floundering/Down to Kill Roy.'

And so he would write prose paragraphs and prose sentences that way, in his own speech rhythms, in chosen American speech rhythms. If you don't write your own prose out as part of your own body rhythm, some actual rhythm from real speech, as some really spoken tale as might be spoken by Homer or any old taleteller, you wind up with an impersonal prose, a prose that doesn't proceed from anybody, and thus a kind of bureaucratic prose or a fictional prose that comes from an assignment, an assignment to make money, or a publishing company, or a magazine; you wind up with an hallucination of prose, rather than an actual piece of prose as it issues from the human body.

In other words you can wind up with prose which is a lie, which doesn't represent anything you or anybody else or any human body actually thinks, but only represents a style of prose that is commercially viable or written in a marketplace of plastic political artifacts. All you have to do is look at Nixon's prose style as 'prose style' to realize that it does not proceed from his physical body, but proceeds from a composite of information-serving bureaucrats—not personal, but representing any individual human spirit as manifested in a single body.

That's a digression. The main point I was trying to make was that there is a tradition of prose in America, including Thomas Wolfe and going through Kerouac, which is personal, in which the prose sentence is completely personal, comes from the writer's own person—his person defined as his body, his breathing rhythm, his actual talk. And the word *person* there I'm taking from the context of Walt Whitman, who talks about 'What we need is large conscious American Persons,' as distinct from objects, or citizens, or subjects, or ciphers, or nonentities, or marketing-research digits.

Kerouac then got more and more personal in his prose, and finally decided that he would write big books without even having a plot, but just write what was going on, without like an 'impersonally' constructed plot, impersonal to his life. He would just write a book in his own persona, as if he were telling his best friend the story of what they did together in a five-year period of running around the country in automobiles.

So he wrote a long book called *On the Road*, and his project was to sit down, using a single piece of paper, like a teletype roll that he got from the United Press office in New York (which is like hundreds and hundreds of feet) and sit down and type away as fast as he could everything he always thought of, going chronologically, about a series of cross-country automobile trips he and a couple buddies took, with all their girls, and the grass they were smokin' in '48–'49–'50 and the peyote they were eating then, and the motel traveling salesmen they met, the small-town redneck gas station attendants they stole gas from, the small-town lonely waitresses they seduced, the confusions they went through, and the visionary benzedrine hallucinations they had from driving a long time on benzedrine, several days, until they began getting visions of shrouded strangers along the road saying 'Woe on America,' and disappearing, flitting like phantoms.

So what he did was try to write it all out, as fast as it came to his mind, all the associations; the style being as if he were telling a tale, excitedly, all night long, staying up all night with his best friend. The prose style being modeled on two buddies telling each other their most intimate secrets excitedly, the long confessional of everything that happened, with every detail, every cunt-hair in the grass included, every tiny eyeball flick of orange neon flashed past in Chicago by the bus station included—in other words, all the back-of-the-brain imagery, which would require, then, sentences that did not necessarily follow exact classic-type syntactical order, but which allowed for interruption with dashes—allowed for the sentences to break in half, take another direction (with parentheses that might go on for paragraphs)—allowed for individual sentences that might not come to their period except after several pages of self-reminiscence, interruption and piling-on of detail, so that what you arrived at was a sort of stream of consciousness, except visioned around a specific subject (the tale of the road being told) and a specific viewpoint, a personal viewpoint, that is, two buddies talking to each other late at night—maybe high on benny or else beer, or just smokin' together—but meeting and recognizing each other like Dostoyevsky characters and telling each other the tale of their childhood or . . .

But then Kerouac finished the book, which was not published for almost a decade after it was finished, and was dissatisfied because he had tied his mind down to fixing it in strictly chronological account. He'd tied his mind down to chronology, and so he was always halting his sentences and stopping to go back to keep it chronological so that if an orange neon light from Chicago intruded on a purple martini glass in neon over a Denver bar ten years earlier, he included the purple neon Denver bar martini glass though he was still trying to keep it up chronologically and tell what happened in Chicago.

So he decided to write another book, which has never been published, his greatest book, called *Visions of Cody*,* which deals with the same main character in about five hundred pages. But called *Visions of Cody*, meaning instead of doing it chronologically, do it in sequence, as recollection of the most beautiful, epiphanous moments. Visionary moments being the structure of the novel—in other words each sentence or chapter being a specific epiphanous heartrending moment no matter where it fell in time, and then going to the center of that moment, the specific physical description of what was

Visions of Cody was published in 1973, with an introduction by Allen Ginsberg.

happening. One, in particular: two guys taking a piss next to each other in a bar in Denver and having a long conversation and one says to the other 'I love you.' Which was like one tender moment between them of a real frank meeting of feelings. A second moment being both of them in Mexico and one taking the car leaving the other guy sick, to get home hitchhiking, 'cause there wasn't enough money and Kerouac had to go home and see his mama. So that was the second epiphany. A third epiphany was the main hero with his wife and children in California with his wife yellin' at him, saying that he's a creep, he's always running away, like he's never at home when the wife needs him, when the children need him, that he's always bringing chicks back to fuck in the attic, and he's always smokin' grass and that all the men runnin' around together are puttin' women down, and so tearing him apart, with neighbor wife girl friends in, all of them finally attacking the guy who was originally the hero of the book. And him going out alone, totally torn down.

But then as he was trying to write out of his present consciousness about the epiphany remembered, and as the prose became more and more elongated, he found that after a while his present consciousness of language would obtrude over even the epiphany subject matter: the subject matter itself would begin disappearing, and that he would hear the babble of language in his head, sometimes associated with the epiphany, and sometimes taking off from it and going into, like, Bach fugues of language rhythm without any kind of reference, necessarily, just syllable after syllable 'ogmogaged-dablab, sabadabuv' but still maintaining the same 'Whapby/Extry special' language, 'bopgooglemop' part of it, so continuing into one pure syllabic 'mop mop mop' after another. So then that novel continues with a hundred pages of pure sound as prose. Then the exact transcription of taped conversations many nights between him and hero . . . then it goes into a 'heavenly imitation' of the tape, then the prose reconstructs itself and comes back to narrative form and describes a scene with the wife yelling at the husband in the end. And that goes on for two hundred pages or so, or a hundred pages, and I think at the end—I haven't read it for many years, I read it in '55—at the end, there's sumpin' that really impressed Robert Duncan, who also saw the novel in the early fifties, 'cause it ends with the hero going out alone, walking past his car by a gas station downtown San Francisco, going out for a pack of beer, I guess, and as he goes out he sees the flash on the highly polished fender of his car of a barber shop mirror, mirrored in the fender of the car, the mirror in the barber shop window mirroring the neon light of a purple martini glass and an orange light from a supermarket across the street, plus a star I guess enters in, or a moon, curved on the fender so making it odd shapes, illusory shapes, and suddenly has like a moment of realization that all nature around him is a total illusory mirror within mirror within mirror, bent out of shape, which he's perceiving, and so Kerouac has a fifty-page description of the contents of the visual imagery on the fender of the automobile. And Duncan, when he saw that, said, like, 'He must be a great genius—he's the only one I know who could write fifty pages on what a polished automobile fender looks like, and have it all make sense.'

Q: Did you read all of that book as sounds?

AG: Oh yeah, aloud, lot of it. Yeah, it's beautiful. Sound is a physical thing that you can play with, if you're interested in sounds, if you're interested in music.

Q: Why hasn't this book of Kerouac's been published?

AG: Oh, I don't know; there was only one copy of it around. After *On the Road* came out he probably should have published that but his editor, Malcolm Cowley—the great litterateur, friend of Hart Crane and novelists of the twenties and thirties—said 'Jack, why don't you write a sort of nice, simple-sentenced book so people can understand your ideas, you know, so it won't be so confusing to people reading it, you know, something for people to appreciate you. You're well-known now, your book will be out, but why don't you write something with short sentences?' So Kerouac took it as a chal-

189

lenge and did write a great little classic called *Dharma Bums*, with short sentences, like haikus, actually.

Thus this longer, more extraordinary piece of prose visions makes the breakthrough for Kerouac's development just as Gertrude Stein's great prose experiment, *The Making of Americans*, stands for her. A thousand pages of insane consciousness babble. I don't know if you know that text. Does anybody know of *The Making of Americans* by Gertrude Stein? That's actually I think one of the great prose masterpieces of the century. Stein had intentions very similar to those I've ascribed to Kerouac—she was a student of William James at Harvard, a student of consciousness, a psychedelic expert, so to speak, to join it to a familiar reference point for you; she was interested in modalities of consciousness, and she was interested in art as articulation of different modalities of consciousness, and she was interested in prose composition as a form of meditation, like yoga.

And, like yoga, she was interested in the language as pure prayer-meditation, removed perhaps even from its associations. To give an example (if this is too abstract and complicated an idea), like Alfred, Lord Tennyson, in order to get himself in an hypnotic state would repeat the name 'Alfred Lord Tennyson; Alfred Lord Tennyson; Alfred Lord Tennyson; Alfred Lord Tennyson; Alfred Lord Tennyson; Alfred Lord Tennyson; Alfred Lord Tennyson; Alfred Lord Tennyson; Alfred Lord Tennyson; Alfred Lord Tennyson; Alfred Lord Tennyson; Alfred Lord Tennyson,' until the sounds no longer had any association but were just pure sounds in a spacious physical universe, and he would get into a funny kind of ecstatic egoless state that way.

So Gertrude Stein was interested in using prose in the same way, that it both have a meaning and at the same time be completely removed from meaning and just become pure rhythmic structures pronounceable aloud. If you ever get a chance, you can listen to a record she made on Caedmon reciting some little prose compositions about Matisse and Picasso where she has little things like 'Napoleon ate ice cream on Elba. Napoleon ate Elba on ice cream. Napoleon ate ice on

Elba cream. Napoleon ate on cream Elba ice. On Napoleon ice ate cream Elba. On Elba ate Napoleon ice cream. Ice cream ate Napoleon on Elba.' Little formulas that go round, round the world, which is how she arrived at her famous statement which as you all know is 'A rose is a rose is a rose.' That's the end of long, long pages of circular prose that exhausts the word *rose* in many different syntactical combinations.

Her great book, *The Making of Americans*, is an examination of the consciousness of one single family. Very few people have read it through, including me—I haven't. I've read, you know, page upon page of it, and read aloud it's really exquisite.

Q: Is that the only way you read fiction—aloud?

AG: No, no, not the *only* way, but what I'm pointing to is that that's a dimension of prose that during a very short period of human history was ignored entirely. In other words, originally, before there was writing, tales, epics, and stories were told aloud. The Australian aborigines, for example, have the most complex system of epics, 'cause they don't have regular writing—it's all mnemonic devices, and they have very, very complicated rituals in their heads which they pronounce aloud, you know. Long things, thousands of pages, if they were measured by pages.

Homer was not written down, originally, remember. The novel never did come out basically until the printing press. And the kind of prose that we're used to now, which is not even spoken aloud but which is read silently by the eye-page mind, is only a McLuhanite excrescence of our immediate civilization, which may not last very long, anyway—they say it's not going to last beyond the next thirty years anyhow. So if you're preparing immortal, deathless prose you'd better pay attention to the sounds, because it's something that will have to be sounded aloud in memory as well as be able to be printed.

Unless you assume that all that machinery and printing press and electricity is going to survive the century—which it may or may not. But in any case, if it exists within the dimension of sound as well as on the page, you're sure you've got more backbone to it, and you're sure that it's more real.

191

I'm interested in prose which can be read aloud, which is real speech, speech which is speakable,—not too removed from sumpin' that somebody would say for real.

Q: On these fifty pages, in *Visions of Cody* where it's primarily audible—

AG: Auditory—yes.

Q: Auditory—something like music—is there anything like a Joycean element?

AG: Yes, of course there are themes that emerge. I mean you couldn't possibly write fifty pages of babble without having your obsessional themes emerge anyway. You'd have to be some sort of strange genius like Gertrude Stein to finally remove *all* association from the language. She made experiments in trying to do that; she never could, quite. She got so much into it that she was really trying to refine it to a point where there *was* no association—just like painters, you know, making an abstract painting, so making an abstract sound pattern. It's pretty hard to remove meaning. You'd have to be a super prose yogi to do that—have to practice for years before you could really get rid of the meaning. You can do it superficially, you know, like a jock Greek joke, some little funny composition. Usually if you assign people to write something that has no meaning you'll find that instead they write something which has all sorts of weird *double entendres*.

But no, I think it wasn't that Kerouac couldn't do the same thing with regular meaning prose; it was that he was suddenly aware of the sound of language, and got swimming in the seas of sound, got lost swimming in the seas of sound, and guided his intellect on sound rather than on dictionary associations with the meanings of the sounds. In other words, another kind of intelligence—still consciousness, still reasonable, but another kind of reason, a reason founded on sounds rather than a reason founded on conceptual associations. If you can use the word reason for that. Or a 'modality of consciousness.'

PARK HONAN

A BEAT PRECURSOR: NELSON ALGREN

Thirteen years ago [1951] Nelson Algren came down Division Street and found himself at the University of Chicago.

I have no idea how he made *that* physical and psychic leap; but there he was. After James T. Farrell, the Most Famous Living Writer of Chicago, rubbing his forehead apprehensively as he eyed two dozen aspirants to Literary Glory spoon-fed Aristotle and Henry James, he must have wondered whether his fee was worth it.

He was a Writer in Residence. Presumably that meant in a small classroom with Gothic windows and a blackboard teaching University of Chicago students for ten or twelve weeks how to write.

That first day he looked at us wanly and I felt sorry for him.

Poor Algren, here he was, a sad-eyed dolphin on Hutchins Beach miles from the deep green teeming immensity of West Madison Street's living Gulf. And here *we* were, I and my classmates, wiping our eye-glasses and dating our notepads, curious to find out (on the beach) what the sea is like and how a dolphin swims.

'Sir,' asked one of our boldest after an awkward hour (a lad who had learned to imitate Ernest Hemingway's style so well that we called him 'Hemingway Hubbles' and felt he had fine literary promise)—'Sir, isn't it true that the autobiographical motive is not always connected to creativity?'

Algren looked startled.

'For example,' Hubbles added to be helpful, 'what about Henry James?'

Algren's hand went slowly through his hair. Then both hands came down gripping the desk in front of them as if the Dolphin were about to shoot up through the skylight.

'I don't know,' replied Chicago's Second Greatest Novelist. His voice had found a mildness now that it retained throughout the course. 'You see, Sonny, I haven't read any Henry James.'

193

I suppose we were shocked. This was heresy of the blackest sort. *Everybody* here read Henry James, and the University as cultural arbiter could do no cultural wrong ('It is not a very good university,' our Chancellor was telling us at the time, 'but it is the best there is')—and so how did it ever let Algren in? And how were we, who were really Serious Writers, to take him?

Chicago and America—in the manner of Algren's former students and the great university itself—have long since learned to take Nelson Algren rather easily. Perhaps he is not very genteel (not for the Henry James lover) but then he is 'the poet of the maimed and socially blighted,' as R.V. Cassill writes. If once we wondered how to classify him, we know now that he 'represents a solid and enduring part of the American heritage of dissent,' as Maxwell Geismar, himself no Henry James lover, cheerfully maintains. (On the shelf with Justice Oliver Wendell Holmes.) If sharply-etched portraits of Chicago's riff-raff in the *Never Come Morning* or the *Neon Wilderness* stories made us feel that Algren's riff-raff were human beings, warm and real and respectable as we, or made us suspect that American urban society was the neon wilderness from which they could not escape and to which morning never comes, then we (who, after all, find dope and delinquency opprobrious) finally can take heart in finding in Algren simply a Poet of the Unfortunate.

He does not arouse us to action or to new awareness any more to judge from his press notices. Cantankerous he is; but what poet is not? And isn't this exemplar of the dissenting heritage even a bit dull, criticize us though he does? (Like that nice old lamented dissenter Robert Frost?)

'I don't find him so controversial,' writes Charles Purvis of Algren's newest book, in the *Chicago Tribune*, a newspaper Algren witheringly attacks and deflates in it. 'Altho he concerns himself mostly with unpleasantness, there is bitter truth in what he says. But these discoveries are not surprising, the imperfections he finds in his narrowed perspective must have been noted by most persons in just passing along life's route.'

(Does Purvis agree with Algren that the *Tribune* is one of these 'imperfections'?)

Van Allen Bradley, Literary Editor of the *Daily News*, is more troubled. The man has dazzling gifts as a novelist, but why, Bradley wonders, does Algren persist in dealing 'with matters that seem to be pretty inconsequential' such as 'the shallowness of contemporary life'? Everybody ought to know that 'the shallowness of contemporary life' is inconsequential stuff for a major novelist to work with. Of course, one must conclude, Jane Austen, W. M. Thackeray, Honore de Balzac, and James Joyce all went astray in forgetting that they should not meddle with 'the shallowness of contemporary life' in their major novels; but Algren ought to know better.

The truth is that we like Nelson Algren now. We like him because we know what to do with him. We can take a trenchant indictment of Chicago such as *The Man with the Golden Arm* for a Hollywood biography of Frank Sinatra and praise the story itself in our most conservative journals for its splendid pathos. If we have an academic turn of mind we can call *A Walk on the Wild Side* a fine example of how 'the materials and attitudes of responsible naturalism' can be converted into 'pure expressionism' and go on to laud the author's noble 'rage'. Even if we are simpleminded we can find something to do with Algren 'the poet'. He is a grand phrase-maker, a touching lyricist of the bedraggled and the destitute, whose poignant little lines—'for keeps and a single day,' 'goodbye for keeps and a day,' 'and Chicago runs from coast to coast'—keep running through his stories and our heads.

So it is that his latest full-length book, *Who Lost an American?* (1963), while nowhere quite condemned is nowhere quite praised. One finds no evidence that any reviewer for the Chicago press has read the book carefully enough to find out what it is about. The *Tribune*, cozily implying that everything Algren says is true but old hat, stands for the rest. Algren ought not to be ignored; but he ought not to be read too closely, either.

To the shelf with him, then, quickly . . . over my stuffed

owl, under my Thoreau, on the knotty-pine tier with the American Dissenters.

But the author of *The Man with the Golden Arm* makes strange company on that shelf.

Algren is not a 'dissenter' so much as he is a severe and light-bringing interpreter of our urban society. Normally, he does not disagree with established opinions, but draws attention to realities about which we express either the vaguest of opinions or no opinion at all.

Who Lost an American?—which may strike you halfway through as a combination travel-book and Norman Mailerish advertisement for Algren—is about neither travel nor Algren, really. It is a book about a process of search and discovery. The search is for the meaning of the human failure of the American city. The discovery is of certain principles that tentatively explain why the richest nation on earth still has its West Madison Streets and Division Streets, its junkies and winos, its effete literary circles and isolated intellectuals, its fat *Playboy* enterprises and morally flabby Bunny Girl oglers. (The Playboy Clubs are symptomatic of a deeper vacuum.)

The search has been a lifelong one for Algren, and we have accompanied him upon it in novels and stories where the shadowy author points a finger toward realities we have not before fully seen or fully understood. But in *Who Lost an American?* we watch Algren himself. The spectacle is funny, lively, unpredictable, and sobering. It takes some agility just to watch. For Algren's intention is not to detail his appearances in the Dublin or Paris he visits, but to show us how the world strikes the consciousness of one normal idiosyncratic man bent upon discovering why his own city is less than humane.

The tour begins in New York. Algren, caught up in imbecilities of the book-publishing capital, enters a Wonderland madder than Alice's. Attired in 'ankle-high white sneakers,' earned by making a bet on a Cuban middleweight, he is the maddest of the Mad Hatters encountered. He jumps for joy in his Ked Gavilans. He meets writers (Norman Manlifellow, Boyish Author, or Giovanni Johnson the Professional Negro), publishers (Mr. McCowardly or Alfred Paperfish, Leading

Footnote King), visits agencies and agents (Doubledge, Dead-sinch & O'Lovingly and Rapietta Greensponge)—all cheerily *non compos barracuda*, as one of them admits—and has the time of his life. His agent at last bundles him off on the 'S. S. Meyer Davis' for a tour of the world. Obligingly, he buys an electrified tie on Eighth Avenue before he sails. This is sad and real enough, for the satire, though feather-light, is finely barbed. Algren's 'New York' is literary America—wonderland of dollar and martini, where self-display substitutes for self-discovery, authorial pretension for authorial patience, Who-you-know for What-you-know.

Later, aboard the great ship, surrounded by the inane babble of First Class escapees from a monotone land, he perceives in a dream where we are headed:

'And downward and downward through deeps ever darker, sun-green to death-green to ultimate black, in the shroud of the waters I felt the hull seeking its sea-bottom home. I felt the hull touch, that gradual impact: then the slow-cutting sand-spraying slide through coral and anemone, along the sea-drifted sands.'

Americans, he believes, have changed from being 'first person' people to being 'third person' non-entities; our lack in individual commitment is noticed everywhere. We join obvious crusades. We prosecute B-girls, drug-addicts, and panhandlers. But who speaks out against the corrupt court, the unjust law, the irresponsible journal, the well-heeled commercial exploiter? We must wait for all the sirens to sound before we sound our own. We flock to Playboy Clubs (where Hefner protects us from emotional involvement with the Bunnies) and Do-Good Organizations (where conscience is satisfied but anonymity safe-guarded). Our poets write in terms of 'We' and 'Us', despite the fact that art cannot be asserted except in terms of 'I'. 'We have no great poet here,' Algren notes in Chicago, 'because there is no real belief in poetry. And in this lack of belief our true corruption lies: not in the hearts of heroin pushers or prostitutes, but in a consciencelessness bred of affluence.'

Who Lost an American? is a 'first person' book. Its tone is by no means uniformly philosophic. It is rich with the prejudices of Nelson Algren. *Time* (and 'Clare Luce Tooth'), *Life, Look, Reader's Digest*, the play *Raisin in the Sun*, elements of the Negro press, American academia, and the Chicago newspaper world *in toto*, are denounced. No reader will agree with the conclusions about all of them; but no reader is expected to. Algren flouts no man or institution not capable of an articulate reply. He does not denigrate dummies—compassion is shown for Banana-Nose Bonura who once made three errors on a single play; but none for a *Daily News* journalist who once made six in one sentence. His object is to expose the pusillanimity, smugness, and vanity of those who are capable of encouraging us to think, act, and feel as an 'I' people—as a nation of concerned individuals—and who utterly fail to do so.

Urban man—believing in nothing, sheltering himself in emotional isolationism from the true problems of life in his city, refusing to risk himself in disciplined self-assertion—is cheered faintly by the vision of a mile-high Frank Lloyd Wright super-perfect metropolis of the future. No doubt, Algren concedes, that horror shall come if we wish it. And what will its anonymous citizenry think of Nelson Algren?

'On the day that the double-tiered causeway is merged with the expressway that merges with the coast-to-coast thruway making right-hand turns every mile into a hundred solid miles of mile-high sky-scrapers, each rising a mile hope-high to the sky out of a mile dream-deep in earth,' he replies, 'my name will not be brought up.'

No doubt, it will not be. *Who Lost an American?* and the novels and the short-stories will gather anonymous dust on the honoring shelves.

But, until then, we may read him—and possibly for more than the poignant poetry of Division Street. After all, he is not a very great writer, but he is one of the best there is.

KENNETH REXROTH

DISENGAGEMENT: THE ART OF THE BEAT GENERATION

Literature generally, but literary criticism in particular, has always been an area in which social forces assume symbolic guise, and work out—or at least exemplify—conflicts taking place in the contemporary, or rather, usually the just-past wider arena of society. Recognition of this does not imply the acceptance of any general theory of social or economic determinism. It is a simple, empirical fact. Because of the pervasiveness of consent in American society generally, that democratic leveling up or down so often bewailed since de Tocqueville, American literature, especially literary criticism, has usually been ruled by a 'line'. The fact that it was spontaneously evolved and enforced only by widespread consent has never detracted from its rigor—but rather the opposite. It is only human to kick against the prodding of an Erich Auerbach or an Andrey Zhdanov. An invisible, all-enveloping compulsion is not likely to be recognized, let alone protested against.

After World War I there was an official line for general consumption: 'Back to Normalcy.' Day by day in every way, we are getting better and better. This produced a literature which tirelessly pointed out that there was nothing whatsoever normal about us. The measure of decay in thirty years is the degree of acceptance of the official myth today—from the most obscure hack on a provincial newspaper to the loftiest metaphysicians of the literary quarterlies. The line goes: 'The generation of experimentation and revolt is over.' This is an etherealized corollary of the general line: 'The bull market will never end.'

I do not wish to argue about the bull market, but in the arts nothing could be less true. The youngest generation is in a state of revolt so absolute that its elders cannot even recognize it. The disaffiliation, alienation, and rejection of the young has, as far as their elders are concerned, moved out of the visible spectrum altogether. Critically invisible, modern revolt, like X-rays and radioactivity, is perceived only by its effects at more materialistic social levels, where it is called delinquency.

'Disaffiliation,' by the way, is the term used by the critic and poet, Lawrence Lipton, who has written several articles on this subject, the first of which, in the *Nation*, quoted as epigraph, 'We disaffiliate . . .' —John L. Lewis.

Like the pillars of Hercules, like two ruined Titans guarding the entrance to one of Dante's circles, stand two great dead juvenile delinquents—the heroes of the post-war generation: the great saxophonist, Charlie Parker, and Dylan Thomas. If the word deliberate means anything, both of them certainly deliberately destroyed themselves.

Both of them were overcome by the horror of the world in which they found themselves, because at last they could no longer overcome that world with the weapon of a purely lyrical art. Both of them were my friends. Living in San Francisco I saw them seldom enough to see them with a perspective which was not distorted by exasperation or fatigue. So as the years passed, I saw them each time in the light of an accelerated personal conflagration.

The last time I saw Bird, at Jimbo's Bob City, he was so gone—so blind to the world—that he literally sat down on me before he realized I was there. 'What happened, man?' I said, referring to the pretentious 'Jazz Concert.' 'Evil, man, evil,' he said, and that's all he said for the rest of the night. About dawn he got up to blow. The rowdy crowd chilled into stillness and the fluent melody spiraled through it.

The last time I saw Dylan, his self-destruction had not just passed the limits of rationality. It had assumed the terrifying inertia of inanimate matter. Being with him was like being swept away by a torrent of falling stones.

Now Dylan Thomas and Charlie Parker have a great deal more in common than the same disastrous end. As artists, they were very similar. They were both very fluent. But this fluent, enchanting utterance had, compared with important artists of the past, relatively little content. Neither of them got very far beyond a sort of entranced rapture at his own creativity. The principal theme of Thomas's poetry was the ambivalence of birth and death—the pain of blood-stained creation. Music, of course, is not so explicit an art, but anybody who knew Charlie Parker knows that he felt much the same way about his own gift. Both of them did communicate one central theme: Against the ruin of the world, there is only one defense—the creative act. This, of course, is the theme of much art—perhaps most poetry. It is the theme of Horace, who certainly otherwise bears little resemblance to Parker or Thomas. The difference is that Horace accepted his theme with a kind of silken assurance. To Dylan and Bird it was an agony and terror. I do not believe that this is due to anything especially frightful about their relationship to their own creativity. I believe rather that it is due to the catastrophic world in which that creativity seemed to be the sole value. Horace's column of imperishable verse shines quietly enough in the lucid air of Augustan Rome. Art may have been for him the most enduring, orderly, and noble activity of man. But the other activities of his life partook of these values. They did not actively negate them. Dylan Thomas's verse had to find endurance in a world of burning cities and burning Jews. He was able to find meaning in his art as long as it was the answer to air raids and gas ovens. As the world began to take on the guise of an immense air raid or gas oven, I believe his art became meaningless to him. I think all this could apply to Parker just as well, although, because of the nature of music, it is not demonstrable—at least not conclusively.

Thomas and Parker have more in common than theme, attitude, life pattern. In the practice of their art, there is an obvious technical resemblance. Contrary to popular belief, they were not great technical innovators. Their effects are only superficially startling. Thomas is a regression from the technical originality and ingenuity of writers like Pierre Reverdy or Apollinaire. Similarly, the innovations of bop, and of Parker particularly, have been vastly overrated by people unfamiliar with music, especially by that ignoramus, the intellectual jitterbug, the jazz aficionado. The tonal novelties consist in the introduction of a few chords used in classical music for centuries. And there is less rhythmic difference between progressive jazz, no matter how progressive, and Dixieland, than there is between two movements of many conventional symphonies.

What Parker and his contemporaries—Gillespie, Davis, Monk, Roach (Tristano is an anomaly), etc.—did was to absorb the musical ornamentation of older jazz into the basic structure, of which it then became an integral part, and with which it then developed. This is true of the melodic line which could be put together from selected passages of almost anybody—Benny Carter, Johnny Hodges. It is true of the rhythmic pattern in which the beat shifts continuously, or at least is continuously sprung, so that it becomes ambiguous enough to allow the pattern to be dominated by the long pulsations of the phrase or strophe. This is exactly what happened in the transition from baroque to rococo music. It is the difference between Bach and Mozart.

It is not a farfetched analogy to say that this is what Thomas did to poetry. The special syntactical effects of a Rimbaud or an Edith Sitwell—actually ornaments—become the main concern. The metaphysical conceits, which fascinate the Reactionary Generation still dominant in backwater American colleges, were embroideries. Thomas's ellipses and ambiguities are ends in themselves. The immediate theme, if it exists, is incidental, and his main theme—the terror of birth—is simply reiterated.

This is one difference between Bird and Dylan which should be pointed out. Again, contrary to popular belief, there is nothing crazy or frantic about Parker either musically or emotionally. His sinuous melody is a sort of naïve transcendence of all experience. Emotionally it does not resemble Berlioz or Wagner; it resembles Mozart. This is true also of a painter like Jackson Pollock. He may have been eccentric in his behavior, but his paintings are as impassive as Persian tiles. Partly this difference is due to the nature of verbal communication. The insistent talk-aboutiveness of the general environment obtrudes into even the most idyllic poetry. It is much more a personal difference. Thomas certainly wanted to tell people about the ruin and disorder of the world. Parker and Pollock wanted to substitute a work of art for the world.

Technique pure and simple, rendition, is not of major importance, but it is interesting that Parker, following Lester Young, was one of the leaders of the so-called saxophone revolution. In modern jazz, the saxophone is treated as a woodwind and played with conventional embouchure. Metrically, Thomas's verse was extremely conventional, as was, incidentally, the verse of that other tragic enragé, Hart Crane.

I want to make clear what I consider the one technical development in the first wave of significant post-war arts. Ornament is confabulation in the interstices of structure. A poem by Dylan Thomas, a saxophone solo by Charles Parker, a painting by Jackson Pollock—these are pure confabulations as ends in themselves. Confabulation has come to determine structure. Uninhibited lyricism should be distinguished from its exact opposite—the sterile, extraneous invention of the corn-belt metaphysicals, our present blight of poetic professors.

Just as Hart Crane had little influence on anyone except very reactionary writers—like Allen Tate, for instance, to whom Valéry was the last word in modern poetry and the felicities of an Apollinaire, let alone a Paul Éluard were nonsense—so Dylan Thomas's influence has been slight indeed. In fact, his only disciple—the only person to imitate his style—was W. S. Graham, who seems to have imitated him without much understanding, and who has since moved on to other methods. Thomas's principal influence lay in the communication of an attitude—that of the now extinct British romantic school of the New Apocalypse—Henry Treece, J. F. Hendry, and others—all of whom were quite conventional poets.

Parker certainly had much more of an influence. At one time it was the ambition of every saxophone player in every high school band in America to blow like Bird. Even before his death this influence had begun to ebb. In fact, the whole generation of the founding fathers of bop—Gillespie, Monk, Davis, Blakey, and the rest—are just now at a considerable discount. The main line of development today goes back to Lester Young and by-passes them.

The point is that many of the most impressive developments in the arts nowadays are aberrant, idiosyncratic. There is no longer any sense of continuing development of the sort that can be traced from Baudelaire to Éluard, or for that matter, from Hawthorne through Henry James to Gertrude Stein. The cubist generation before World War I, and, on a lower level, the surrealists of the period between the wars, both assumed an accepted universe of discourse, in which, to quote André Breton, it was possible to make definite advances, exactly as in the sciences. I doubt if anyone holds such ideas today. Continuity exists, but like the neo-swing music developed from Lester Young, it is a continuity sustained by popular demand.

In the plastic arts, a very similar situation exists. Surrealists like Hans Arp and Max Ernst might talk of creation by hazard—of composing pictures by walking on them with painted soles, or by tossing bits of paper up in the air. But it is obvious that they were self-deluded. Nothing looks anything like an Ernst or an Arp but another Ernst or Arp. Nothing looks less like their work than the happenings of random occasion. Many of the post-World War II abstract expressionists, apostles of the discipline of spontaneity and hazard, look alike, and do look like accidents. The aesthetic appeal of pure paint laid on at random may exist, but it is a very impoverished appeal. Once again what has happened is an all-consuming confabulation of the incidentals, the accidents of painting. It is curious that at its best, the work of this school of painting—Mark Rothko, Jackson Pollock, Clyfford Still, Robert Motherwell, Willem deKooning, and the rest—resembles nothing so much as the passage painting of quite unimpressive painters: the mother-of-pearl shimmer in the background of a Henry McFee, itself a formula derived from Renoir; the splashes of light and black which fake drapery in the fashionable imitators of Hals and Sargent. Often work of this sort is presented as calligraphy—the pure utterance of the brush stroke seeking only absolute painteresque values. You have only to compare such painting with the work of, say, Sesshu, to realize that someone is using words and brushes carelessly.

At its best the abstract expressionists achieve a simple rococo decorative surface. Its poverty shows up immediately when compared with Tiepolo, where the rococo rises to painting of extraordinary profundity and power. A Tiepolo painting, however confabulated, is a universe of tensions in vast depths. A Pollock is an object of art—bijouterie—disguised only by its great size. In fact, once the size is big enough to cover a whole wall, it turns into nothing more than extremely expensive wallpaper. Now there is nothing wrong with complicated wallpaper. There is just more to Tiepolo. The great Ashikaga brush painters painted wallpapers, too—at least portable ones, screens.

A process of elimination which leaves the artist with nothing but the play of his materials themselves cannot sustain interest in either artist or public for very long. So, in the last couple of years, abstract expressionism has tended toward romantic suggestion—indications of landscape or living figures. This approaches the work of the Northwest school—Clayton Price, Mark Tobey, Kenneth Callahan, Morris Graves—who have of all recent painters come nearest to conquering a territory which painting could occupy with some degree of security. The Northwest school, of course, admittedly is influenced by the ink painters of the Far East, and by Tintoretto and Tiepolo. The dominant school of post-World War II American painting has really been a long detour into plastic nihilism. I should add that painters like Ernie Briggs seem to be opening up new areas of considerable scope within the main traditional abstract expressionism—but with remarkable convergence to Tobey or Tintoretto, as you prefer.

Today American painting is just beginning to emerge with a transvaluation of values. From the mid-nineteenth century on, all ruling standards in the plastic arts were subject to continual attack. They were attacked because each on-coming generation had new standards of their own to put in their place. Unfortunately, after one hundred years of this, there grew up a generation ignorant of the reasons for the revolt of their elders, and without any standards whatever. It has been necessary to create standards anew out of chaos. This is what modern education purports to do with finger painting in nursery schools. This is why the Northwest school has enjoyed such an advantage over the abstract expressionists. Learning by doing, by trial and error, is learning by the hardest way. If you want to overthrow the cubist tradition of architectural painting, it is much easier to seek out its opposites in the history of culture and study them carefully. At least it saves a great deal of time.

One thing can be said of painting in recent years—its revolt, its rejection of the classic modernism of the first half of the century, has been more absolute than in any other art. The only ancestor of abstract expressionism is the early Kandinsky —a style rejected even by Kandinsky himself. The only painter in a hundred years who bears the slightest resemblance to Tobey or Graves is Odilon Redon (perhaps Gustave Moreau a little), whose stock was certainly not very high with painters raised in the cubist tradition.

The ready market for prose fiction—there is almost no market at all for modern painting, and very much less for poetry—has had a decisive influence on its development. Sidemen with Kenton or Herman may make a good if somewhat hectic living, but any novelist who can write home to mother, or even spell his own name, has a chance to become another Brubeck. The deliberately and painfully intellectual fiction which appears in the literary quarterlies is a by-product of certain classrooms. The only significant fiction in America is popular fiction. Nobody realizes this better than the French. To them our late-born imitators of Henry James and E. M. Forster are just *chiens qui fument*, and arithmetical horses and bicycling seals. And there is no more perishable commodity than the middle-brow novel. No one today reads Ethel L. Voynich or Joseph Hergesheimer, just as no one in the future will read the writers' workshop pupils and teachers who fill the literary quarterlies. Very few people, except themselves, read them now.

On the other hand, the connection between the genuine high-brow writer and the genuinely popular is very close.

Hemingway had hardly started to write before his style had been reduced to a formula in *Black Mask*, the first hard-boiled detective magazine. In no time at all he had produced two first-class popular writers, Raymond Chandler and Dashiell Hammett. Van Vechten, their middle-brow contemporary, is forgotten. It is from Chandler and Hammett and Hemingway that the best modern fiction derives; although most of it comes out in hard covers, it is always thought of as written for a typical pocketbook audience. Once it gets into pocketbooks it is sometimes difficult to draw the line between it and its most ephemeral imitators. Even the most *précieux* French critics, a few years ago, considered Horace McCoy America's greatest contemporary novelist. There is not only something to be said for their point of view; the only thing to be said against it is that they don't read English.

Much of the best popular fiction deals with the world of the utterly disaffiliated. Burlesque and carnival people, hipsters, handicappers and hop heads, wanted men on the lam, an expendable squad of soldiers being expended, anyone who by definition is divorced from society and cannot afford to believe even an iota of the social lie—these are the favorite characters of modern post-war fiction, from Norman Mailer to the latest ephemerid called *Caught*, or *Hung Up*, or *The Needle*, its bright cover winking invitingly in the drugstore. The first, and still the greatest, novelist of total disengagement is not a young man at all, but an elderly former I.W.W. of German ancestry, B. Traven, the author of *The Death Ship* and *The Treasure of Sierra Madre*.

It is impossible for an artist to remain true to himself as a man, let alone an artist, and work within the context of this society. Contemporary mimics of Jane Austen or Anthony Trollope are not only beneath contempt. They are literally unreadable. It is impossible to keep your eyes focused on the page. Writers as far apart as J. F. Powers and Nelson Algren agree in one thing—their diagnosis of an absolute corruption.

This refusal to accept the mythology of press and pulpit as a medium for artistic creation, or even enjoyable reading matter, is one explanation for the popularity of escapist literature. Westerns, detective stories and science fiction are all situated beyond the pale of normal living. The slick magazines are only too well aware of this, and in these three fields especially exert steady pressure on their authors to accentuate the up-beat. The most shocking example of this forced perversion is the homey science fiction story, usually written by a woman, in which a one-to-one correlation has been made for the commodity-ridden tale of domestic whimsey, the stand-by of magazines given away in the chain groceries. In writers like Judith Merrill the space pilot and his bride bat the badinage back and forth while the robot maid makes breakfast in the jet-propelled lucite orange squeezer and the electronic bacon rotobroiler, dropping pearls of dry assembly plant wisdom (like plantation wisdom but drier), the whilst. Still, few yield to these pressures, for the obvious reason that fiction indistinguishable from the advertising columns on either side of the page defeats its own purpose, which is to get the reader to turn over the pages when he is told 'continued on p.47.'

Simenon is still an incomparably better artist and psychologist than the psychological Jean Stafford. Ward Moore is a better artist than Eudora Welty, and Ernest Haycox than William Faulkner, just as, long ago, H. G. Wells was a better artist, as artist, than E. M. Forster, as well as being a lot more interesting. At its best, popular literature of this sort, coming up, meets high-brow literature coming down. It has been apparent novel by novel that Nelson Algren is rising qualitatively in this way. In his latest novel, thoroughly popular in its materials, *A Walk on the Wild Side*, he meets and absorbs influences coming down from the top, from the small handful of bona fide high-brow writers working today—Céline, Jean Genêt, Samuel Beckett, Henry Miller. In Algren's case this has been a slow growth, and he has carried his audience with him. Whatever the merits of his subject matter or his thesis—'It is better to be out than in. It is better to be on the lam than on the cover of *Time* Magazine'—his style started out as a distressing mixture of James Farrell and Kenneth Fearing. Only recently has he achieved an idiom of his own.

There is only one thing wrong with this picture, and that is that the high-brow stimulus still has to be imported. Algren, who is coming to write more and more like Céline, has no difficulty selling his fiction. On the other hand, an author like Jack Kerouac, who is in his small way the peer of Céline, Destouches or Beckett, is the most famous 'unpublished' author in America. Every publisher's reader and adviser of any moment has read him and is enthusiastic about him. In other words, anybody emerging from the popular field has every advantage. It is still extremely difficult to enter American fiction from the top down.

The important point about modern fiction is that it is salable, and therefore viable in our society, and therefore successful in the best sense of the word. When a novelist has something to say, he knows people will listen. Only the jazz musician, but to a much lesser degree, shares this confidence in his audience. It is of the greatest social significance that the novelists who say, 'I am proud to be delinquent' are nevertheless sold in editions of hundreds of thousands.

Nobody much buys poetry. I know. I am one of the country's most successful poets. My books actually sell out—in editions of two thousand. Many a poet, the prestige ornament of a publisher's list, has more charges against his royalty account than credits for books sold. The problem of poetry is the problem of communication itself. All art is a symbolic criticism of values, but poetry is specifically and almost exclusively that. A painting decorates the wall. A novel is a story. Music . . . soothes a savage breast. But poetry you have to take straight. In addition, the entire educational system is in a conspiracy to make poetry as unpalatable as possible. From the seventh grade teacher who rolls her eyes and chants H.D. to the seven types of ambiguity factories, grinding out little Donnes and Hopkinses with hayseeds in their hair, everybody is out to de-poetize forever the youth of the land. Again, bad and spurious painting, music, and fiction are not really well-organized, except on obvious commercial levels, where they can be avoided. But in poetry Gresham's Law is supported by the full weight of the powers that be. From about 1930 on, a conspiracy of bad poetry has been as carefully organized as the Communist

Party, and today controls most channels of publication except the littlest of the little magazines. In all other departments of American culture, English influence has been at a steadily declining minimum since the middle of the nineteenth century. In 1929, this was still true of American poetry. Amy Lowell, Sandburg, H.D., Pound, Marianne Moore, William Carlos Williams, Wallace Stevens—all of the major poets of the first quarter of the century owed far more to Apollinaire or Francis Jammes than they did to the whole body of the English tradition. In fact, the new poetry was essentially an anti-English, pro-French movement—a provincial but clear echo of the French revolt against the symbolists. On the other hand, Jules Laforgue and his English disciples, Ernest Dowson and Arthur Symons, were the major influence on T.S. Eliot. Unfortunately Mr. Eliot's poetic practice and his thoroughly snobbish critical essays which owed their great cogency to their assumption, usually correct, that his readers had never heard of the authors he discussed—Webster, Crashaw, or Lancelot Andrewes—lent themselves all too easily to the construction of an academy and the production of an infinite number of provincial academicians—policemen entrusted with the enforcement of Gresham's Law.

Behind the façade of this literary Potemkin village, the main stream of American poetry, with its sources in Baudelaire, Lautréamont, Rimbaud, Apollinaire, Jammes, Reverdy, Salmon, and later Breton and Éluard, has flowed on unperturbed, though visible only at rare intervals between the interstices of the academic hoax. Today the class magazines and the quarterlies are filled with poets as alike as two bad pennies. It is my opinion that these people do not really exist. Most of them are androids designed by Ransom, Tate, and Co., and animated by Randall Jarrell. They are not just counterfeit; they are not even real counterfeits, but counterfeits of counterfeits. On these blurred and clumsy coins the lineaments of Mr. Eliot and I. A. Richards dimly can be discerned, like the barbarized Greek letters which nobody could read on Scythian money.

This is the world in which over every door is written the

slogan: 'The generation of experiment and revolt is over. Bohemia died in the twenties. There are no more little magazines.' Actually there have never been so many little magazines. In spite of the fantastic costs of printing, more people than ever are bringing out little sheets of free verse and making up the losses out of their own pockets. This world has its own major writers, its own discoveries, its own old masters, its own tradition and continuity. Its sources are practically exclusively French, and they are all post-symbolist, even anti-symbolist. It is the Reactionary Generation who are influenced by Laforgue, the symbolists, and Valéry. Nothing is more impressive than the strength, or at least the cohesion, of this underground movement. Poets whom the quarterlies pretend never existed, like Louis Zukovsky and Jack Wheelwright, are still searched out in large libraries or obscure bookshops and copied into notebooks by young writers. I myself have a complete typewritten collection of the pre-reactionary verse of Yvor Winters. And I know several similar collections of 'forgotten modernists' in the libraries of my younger friends. People are always turning up who say something like, 'I just discovered a second-hand copy of Parker Tyler's *The Granite Butterfly* in a Village bookshop. It's great, man.' On the other hand, I seriously doubt whether *The Hudson Review* would ever consider for a moment publishing a line of Parker Tyler's verse. And he is certainly not held up as an example in the Iowa Writers' Workshop. There are others who have disappeared entirely—Charles Snider, Sherry Mangan, R. E. F. Larsson, the early Winters, the last poems of Ford Madox Ford. They get back into circulation, as far as I know, only when I read them to somebody at home or on the air, and then I am always asked for a copy. Some of the old avant garde seem to have written themselves out, for instance, Mina Loy. There are a few established old masters, outstanding of whom are, of course, Ezra Pound and William Carlos Williams. I am not a passionate devotee of Pound myself. In fact, I think his influence is largely pernicious. But no one could deny its extent and power amongst young people today. As for Williams, more and more people, even some of the Reactionary Generation, have come to think of him as our greatest living poet. Even Randall Jarrell and R. P. Blackmur have good words to say for him.

Then there is a middle generation which includes Kenneth Patchen, Jean Garrigue, myself, and a few others—notably Richard Eberhart, who looks superficially as if he belonged with the Tates and Blackmurs but who is redeemed by his directness, simplicity, and honesty, and Robert Fitzgerald and Dudley Fitts. Curiously enough, in the taste of the young, Kenneth Fearing is not included in this group, possibly because his verse is too easy. It does include the major work, for example, *Ajanta*, of Muriel Rukeyser.

I should say that the most influential poets of the youngest established generation of the avant garde are Denise Levertov, Robert Creeley, Charles Olson, Robert Duncan, and Philip Lamantia. The most influential avant garde editor is perhaps Cid Corman, with his magazine *Origin*. Richard Emerson's *Golden Goose* and Robert Creeley's *Black Mountain Review* seem to have suspended publication temporarily. Jonathan Williams, himself a fine poet, publishes the Jargon Press.

All of this youngest group have a good deal in common. They are all more or less influenced by French poetry, and by Céline, Beckett, Artaud, Genêt, to varying degrees. They are also influenced by William Carlos Williams, D. H. Lawrence, Whitman, Pound. They are all interested in Far Eastern art and religion; some even call themselves Buddhists. Politically they are all strong disbelievers in the State, war, and the values of commercial civilization. Most of them would no longer call themselves anarchists, but just because adopting such a label would imply adherence to a 'movement.' Anything in the way of an explicit ideology is suspect. Contrary to gossip of a few years back, I have never met anybody in this circle who was a devotee of the dubious notions of the psychologist, Wilhelm Reich; in fact, few of them have ever read him, and those who have consider him a charlatan.

Although there is wide diversity—Olson is very like Pound; Creeley resembles Mallarmé; Denise Levertov in England was a leading New Romantic, in America she has come under the influence of William Carlos Williams; Robert Duncan has assimilated ancestors as unlike as Gertrude Stein and Éluard, and so on—although this diversity is very marked, there is a strong bond of aesthetic unity too. No avant garde American poet accepts the I. A. Richards-Valéry thesis that a poem is an end in itself, an anonymous machine for providing aesthetic experiences. All believe in poetry as communication, statement from one person to another. So they all avoid the studied ambiguities and metaphysical word play of the Reactionary Generation and seek clarity of image and simplicity of language.

In the years since the war, it would seem as though more and more of what is left of the avant garde has migrated to Northern California. John Berryman once referred to the Lawrence cult of 'mindless California,' and Henry Miller and I have received other unfavorable publicity which has served only to attract people to this area. Mr. Karl Shapiro, for instance, once referred to San Francisco as 'the last refuge of the Bohemian remnant'—a description he thought of as invidious. Nevertheless it is true that San Francisco is today the seat of an intense literary activity not unlike Chicago of the first quarter of the century. A whole school of poets has grown up—almost all of them migrated here from somewhere else. Some of them have national reputations, at least in limited circles. For example, Philip Lamantia among the surrealists; William Everson (Br. Antoninus, O.P.)—perhaps the best Catholic poet. Others have come up recently, like Lawrence Ferlinghetti, Allen Ginsberg, Gary Snyder, Philip Whalen, James Harmon, Michael McClure, and still have largely local reputations. But the strength of these reputations should not be underestimated. The Poetry Center of San Francisco State College, directed by Ruth Witt-Diamant, gives a reading to a large audience at least twice a month. And there are other readings equally well attended every week in various galleries and private homes.

This means that poetry has become an actual social force— something which has always sounded hitherto like a Utopian dream of the William Morris sort. It is a very thrilling experience to hear an audience of more than three hundred people stand and cheer and clap, as they invariably do at a reading by Allen Ginsberg, certainly a poet of revolt if there ever was one.

There is no question but that the San Francisco renaissance is radically different from what is going on elsewhere. There are hand presses, poetry readings, young writers elsewhere—but nowhere else is there a whole younger generation culture pattern characterized by total rejection of the official high-brow culture—where critics like John Crowe Ransom or Lionel Trilling, magazines like the *Kenyon, Hudson* and *Partisan* reviews, are looked on as 'The Enemy'—the other side of the barricades.

There is only one trouble about the renaissance in San Francisco. It is too far away from the literary market place. That, of course, is the reason why the Bohemian remnant, the avant garde have migrated here. It is possible to hear the story about what so-and-so said to someone else at a cocktail party twenty years ago just one too many times. You grab a plane or get on your thumb and hitchhike to the other side of the continent for good and all. Each generation, the great Latin poets came from farther and farther from Rome. Eventually, they ceased to even go there except to see the sights.

Distance from New York City does, however, make it harder to get things, if not published, at least nationally circulated. I recently formed a collection for one of the foundations of avant garde poetry printed in San Francisco. There were a great many items. The poetry was all at least readable, and the hand printing and binding were in most cases very fine indeed. None of these books were available in bookstores elsewhere in the country, and only a few of them had been reviewed in newspapers or magazines with national circulation.

Anyway, as an old war horse of the revolution of the word, things have never looked better from where I sit. The avant garde has not only not ceased to exist. It's jumping all over the place. Something's happening, man.

The disengagement of the creator, who, as creator, is necessarily judge, is one thing, but the utter nihilism of the emptied-out hipster is another. What is going to come of an attitude like this? It is impossible to go on indefinitely saying: 'I am proud to be a delinquent,' without destroying all civilized values. Between such persons no true enduring interpersonal relationships can be built, and of course, nothing resembling a true 'culture'—an at-homeness of men with each other, their work, their loves, their environment. The end result must be the desperation of shipwreck—the despair, the orgies, ultimately the cannibalism of a lost lifeboat. I believe that most of an entire generation will go to ruin—the ruin of Céline, Artaud, Rimbaud, voluntarily, even enthusiastically. What will happen afterwards I don't know, but for the next ten years or so we are going to have to cope with the youth we, my generation, put through the atom smasher. Social disengagement, artistic integrity, voluntary poverty—these are powerful virtues and may pull them through, but they are not the virtues we tried to inculcate—rather they are the exact opposite.

NORMAN PODHORETZ

THE KNOW-NOTHING BOHEMIANS

Allen Ginsberg's little volume of poems, *Howl*, which got the San Francisco renaissance off to a screaming start a year or so ago, was dedicated to Jack Kerouac ('new Buddha of American prose, who spit forth intelligence into eleven books written in half the number of years . . . creating a spontaneous bop prosody and original classic literature'), William Seward Burroughs ('author of *Naked Lunch*, an endless novel which will drive everybody mad'), and Neal Cassady ('author of *The First Third*, an autobiography . . . which enlightened Buddha'). So far, everybody's sanity has been spared by the inability of *Naked Lunch* to find a publisher,* and we may never get the chance to discover what Buddha learned from Neal Cassady's autobiography, but thanks to the Viking and Grove Presses, two of Kerouac's original classics, *On the Road* and *The Subterraneans*, have now been revealed to the world. When *On the Road* appeared last year, Gilbert Milstein commemorated the event in the New York *Times* by declaring it to be 'a historic occasion' comparable to the publication of *The Sun Also Rises* in the 1920's. But even before the novel was actually published, the word got around that Kerouac was the spokesman of a new group of rebels and Bohemians who called themselves the Beat Generation, and soon his photogenic countenance (unshaven, of course, and topped by an unruly crop of rich black hair falling over his forehead) was showing up in various mass-circulation magazines, he was being interviewed earnestly on television, and he was being featured in a Greenwich Village nightclub where, in San Francisco fashion, he read specimens of his spontaneous bop prosody against a background of jazz music.

*Eventually published by the Olympia Press in Paris.

Though the nightclub act reportedly flopped, *On the Road* sold well enough to hit the best-seller lists for several weeks, and it isn't hard to understand why. Americans love nothing so much as representative documents, and what could be more interesting in this Age of Sociology than a novel that speaks for the 'young generation?' (The fact that Kerouac is thirty-five or thereabouts was generously not held against him.) Beyond that, however, I think that the unveiling of the Beat Generation was greeted with a certain relief by many people who had been disturbed by the notorious respectability and 'maturity' of post-war writing. This was more like it—restless, rebellious, confused youth living it up, instead of thin, balding, buttoned-down instructors of English composing ironic verses with one hand while changing the baby's diapers with the other. Bohemianism is not particularly fashionable nowadays, but the image of Bohemia still exerts a powerful fascination—nowhere more so than in the suburbs, which are filled to overflowing with men and women who uneasily think of themselves as conformists and of Bohemianism as the heroic road. The whole point of *Marjorie Morningstar* was to assure the young marrieds of Mamaroneck that they were better off than the apparently glamorous *luftmenschen* of Greenwich Village, and the fact that Wouk had to work so hard at making this idea seem convincing is a good indication of the strength of prevailing doubt on the matter.

On the surface, at least, the Bohemianism of *On the Road* is very attractive. Here is a group of high-spirited young men running back and forth across the country (mostly hitch-hiking, sometimes in their own second-hand cars), going to 'wild' parties in New York and Denver and San Francisco, living on a shoe-string (GI educational benefits, an occasional fifty bucks from a kindly aunt, an odd job as a typist, a fruit-picker, a parking-lot attendant), talking intensely about love and God and salvation, getting high on marijuana (but never heroin or cocaine), listening feverishly to jazz in crowded little joints, and sleeping freely with beautiful girls. Now and again there is a reference to gloom and melancholy, but the characteristic note struck by Kerouac is exuberance:

We stopped along the road for a bite to eat. The cowboy went off to have a spare tire patched, and Eddie and I sat down in a kind of homemade diner. I heard a great laugh, the greatest laugh in the world, and here came this rawhide oldtimes Nebraska farmer with a bunch of other boys into the diner; you could hear his raspy cries clear across the plains, across the whole gray world of them that day. Everybody else laughed with him. He didn't have a care in the world and had the hugest regard for everybody. I said to myself, Wham, listen to that man laugh. That's the West, here I am in the West. He came booming into the diner, calling Maw's name, and she made the sweetest cherry pie in Nebraska, and I had some with a mountainous scoop of ice cream on top. 'Maw, rustle me up some grub afore I have to start eatin myself or some damn silly idee like that.' And he threw himself on a stool and went hyaw hyaw hyaw hyaw. 'And throw some beans in it.' It was the spirit of the West sitting right next to me. I wished I knew his whole raw life and what the hell he'd been doing all these years besides laughing and yelling like that. Whooee, I told my soul, and the cowboy came back and off we went to Grand Island.

Kerouac's enthusiasm for the Nebraska farmer is part of his general readiness to find the source of all vitality and virtue in simple rural types and in the dispossessed urban groups (Negroes, bums, whores). His idea of life in New York is 'millions and millions hustling forever for a buck among themselves . . . grabbing, taking, giving, sighing, dying, just so they could be buried in those awful cemetery cities beyond Long Island City,' whereas the rest of America is populated almost exclusively by the true of heart. There are intimations here of a kind of know-nothing populist sentiment, but in other ways this attitude resembles Nelson Algren's belief that bums and whores and junkies are more interesting than white-collar workers or civil servants. The difference is that Algren hates middle-class respectability for moral and political reasons—the middle class exploits and persecutes—while Kerouac, who is thoroughly unpolitical, seems to feel that respectability is a sign not of moral corruption but of spiritual death. 'The only people for me,' says Sal Paradise, the narrator of *On the Road*, 'are the mad ones, the ones who are mad to live, mad to talk, mad to be saved, desirous of everything at the same time, the ones who never yawn or say a commonplace thing, but burn, burn, burn like fabulous yellow roman candles exploding like spiders across the stars. . . .' This tremendous emphasis on emotional intensity, this notion that to be hopped-up is the most desirable of all human conditions, lies at the heart of the Beat Generation ethos and distinguishes it radically from the Bohemianism of the past.

The Bohemianism of the 1920's represented a repudiation of the provinciality, philistinism, and moral hypocrisy of American life—a life, incidentally which was still essentially small-town and rural in tone. Bohemia, in other words, was a movement created in the name of civilization: its ideals were intelligence, cultivation, spiritual refinement. The typical literary figure of the 1920's was a midwesterner (Hemingway, Fitzgerald, Sinclair Lewis, Eliot, Pound) who had fled from his home town to New York or Paris in search of a freer, more expansive, more enlightened way of life than was possible in Ohio or Minnesota or Michigan. The political radicalism that supplied the characteristic coloring of Bohemianism in the 1930's did nothing to alter the urban, cosmopolitan bias of the 1920's. At its best, the radicalism of the 1930's was marked by deep intellectual seriousness and aimed at a state of society in which the fruits of civilization would be more widely available—and ultimately available to all.

The Bohemianism of the 1950's is another kettle of fish altogether. It is hostile to civilization; it worships primitivism, instinct, energy, 'blood.' To the extent that it has intellectual interests at all, they run to mystical doctrines, irrationalist philosophies, and left-wing Reichianism. The only art the new Bohemians have any use for is jazz, mainly of the cool variety. Their predilection for bop language is a way of demonstrating solidarity with the primitive vitality and spontaneity they find in jazz and of expressing contempt for coherent, rational discourse, which, being a product of the mind, is in their view a form of death. To be articulate is to admit that you have no feelings (for how can real feelings be expressed in syntactical language?), that you can't respond to anything (Kerouac responds to everything by saying 'Wow!'), and that you are probably impotent.

At the one end of the spectrum, this ethos shades off into violence and criminality, main-line drug addiction and madness. Allen Ginsberg's poetry, with its lurid apocalyptic celebration of 'angel-headed hipsters,' speaks for the darker side of the new Bohemianism. Kerouac is milder. He shows little taste for violence, and the criminality he admires is the harmless kind. The hero of *On the Road*, Dean Moriarty, has a record: 'From the age of eleven to seventeen he was usually in reform school. His specialty was stealing cars, gunning for girls coming out of high school in the afternoon, driving them out to the mountains, making them, and coming back to sleep in any available hotel bathtub in town.' But Dean's criminality, we are told, 'was not something that sulked and sneered; it was a wild yea-saying overburst of American joy; it was Western, the west wind, an ode from the Plains, something new, long prophesied, long a-coming (he only stole cars for joy rides).' And, in fact, the species of Bohemian that Kerouac writes about is on the whole rather law-abiding. In *The Subterraneans*, a bunch of drunken boys steal a pushcart in the middle of the night, and when they leave it in front of a friend's apartment building, he denounces them angrily for 'screwing up the security of my pad.' When Sal Paradise (in *On the Road*) steals some groceries from the canteen of an itinerant workers' camp in which he has taken a temporary job as a barracks guard, he comments, 'I suddenly began to realize that everybody in America is a natural-born thief'—which of course is a way of turning his own stealing into a bit of boyish prankishness. Nevertheless, Kerouac is attracted to criminality, and that in itself is more significant than the fact that he personally feels constrained to put the brakes on his own destructive impulses.

Sex has always played a very important role in Bohemianism: sleeping around was the Bohemian's most dramatic demonstration of his freedom from conventional moral standards, and a defiant denial of the idea that sex was permissible only in marriage and then only for the sake of a family. At the same time, to be 'promiscuous' was to assert the validity of sexual experience in and for itself. The 'meaning' of Bohemian sex, then, was at once social and personal, a crucial element in the Bohemian's ideal of civilization. Here again the contrast with Beat Generation Bohemianism is sharp. On the one hand, there is a fair amount of sexual activity in *On the Road* and *The Subterraneans*. Dean Moriarty is a 'new kind of American saint' at least partly because of his amazing sexual power: he can keep three women satisfied simultaneously and he can make love any time, anywhere (once he mounts a girl in the back seat of a car while poor Sal Paradise is trying to sleep in front). Sal, too, is always on the make, and though he isn't as successful as the great Dean, he does pretty well: offhand I can remember a girl in Denver, one on a bus, and another in New York, but a little research would certainly unearth a few more. The heroine of *The Subterraneans*, a Negro girl named Mardou Fox, seems to have switched from one to another member of the same gang and back again ('This has been an incestuous group in its time'), and we are given to understand that there is nothing unusual about such an arrangement. But the point of all this hustle and bustle is not freedom from ordinary social restrictions or defiance of convention (except in relation to homosexuality, which is Ginsberg's preserve: among 'the best minds' of Ginsberg's generation who were destroyed by America are those 'who let themselves be —— in the —— by saintly motorcyclists, and screamed with joy, / who blew and were blown by those human seraphim, the sailors, caresses of Atlantic and Caribbean love'). The sex in Kerouac's books goes hand in hand with a great deal of talk about forming permanent relationships ('although I have a hot feeling sexually and all that for her,' says the poet Adam Moorad in *The Subter-*

raneans, 'I really don't want to get any further into her not only for these reasons but finally, the big one, if I'm going to get involved with a girl now I want to be permanent like permanent and serious and long termed and I can't do that with her'), and a habit of getting married and then duly divorced and re-married when another girl comes along. In fact, there are as many marriages and divorces in *On the Road* as in the Hollywood movie colony (must be that California climate): 'All those years I was looking for the woman I wanted to marry,' Sal Paradise tells us. 'I couldn't meet a girl without saying to myself, What kind of wife would she make?' Even more revealing is Kerouac's refusal to admit that any of his characters ever make love wantonly or lecherously—no matter how casual the encounter it must always entail sweet feelings toward the girl. Sal, for example, is fixed up with Rita Bettencourt in Denver, whom he has never met before. 'I got her in my bedroom after a long talk in the dark of the front room. She was a nice little girl, simple and true [naturally], and tremendously frightened of sex. I told her it was beautiful. I wanted to prove this to her. She let me prove it, but I was too impatient and proved nothing. She sighed in the dark. "What do you want out of life?" I asked, and I used to ask that all the time of girls.' This is rather touching, but only because the narrator is really just as frightened of sex as that nice little girl was. He is frightened of failure and he worries about his performance. For *performance* is the point—performance and 'good orgasms,' which are the first duty of man and the only duty of woman. What seems to be involved here, in short, is sexual anxiety of enormous proportions—an anxiety that comes out very clearly in *The Subterraneans*, which is about a love affair between the young writer, Leo Percepied, and the Negro girl, Mardou Fox. Despite its protestations, the book is one long agony of fear and trembling over sex:

> I spend long nights and many hours making her, finally
> I have her, I pray for it to come, I can hear her
> breathing harder, I hope against hope it's time, a noise
> in the hall (or whoop of drunkards next door) takes her

mind off and she can't make it and laughs—but when she does make it I hear her crying, whimpering, the shuddering electrical female orgasm makes her sound like a little girl crying, moaning in the night, it lasts a good twenty seconds and when it's over she moans, 'O why can't it last longer,' and 'O when will I when you do?'—'Soon now I bet,' I say, 'you're getting closer and closer'—

Very primitive, very spontaneous, very elemental, very beat.

For the new Bohemians interracial friendships and love affairs apparently play the same role of social defiance that sex used to play in older Bohemian circles. Negroes and whites associate freely on a basis of complete equality and without a trace of racial hostility. But putting it that way understates the case, for not only is there no racial hostility, there is positive adulation for the 'happy, true-hearted, ecstatic Negroes of America.'

At lilac evening I walked with every muscle aching among the lights of 27th and Welton in the Denver colored section, wishing I were a Negro, feeling that the best the white world had offered was not enough ecstasy for me, not enough life, joy, kicks, darkness, music, not enough night. . . . I wished I were a Denver Mexican, or even a poor overworked Jap, anything but what I was so drearily, a 'white man' disillusioned. All my life I'd had white ambitions. . . . I passed the dark porches of Mexican and Negro homes; soft voices were there, occasionally the dusky knee of some mysterious sensuous gal; and dark faces of the men behind rose arbors. Little children sat like sages in ancient rocking chairs.

It will be news to the Negroes to learn that they are so happy and ecstatic; I doubt if a more idyllic picture of Negro life has been painted since certain Southern ideologues tried to convince the world that things were just as fine as fine could

223

be for the slaves on the old plantation. Be that as it may, Kerouac's love for Negroes and other dark-skinned groups is tied up with his worship of primitivism, not with any radical social attitudes. Ironically enough, in fact, to see the Negro as more elemental than the white man, as Ned Polsky has acutely remarked is 'an inverted form of keeping the nigger in his place.' But even if it were true that American Negroes, by virtue of their position in our culture, have been able to retain a degree of primitive spontaneity, the last place you would expect to find evidence of this is among Bohemian Negroes. Bohemianism, after all, is for the Negro a means of entry into the world of the whites, and no Negro Bohemian is going to cooperate in the attempt to identify him with Harlem or Dixieland. The only major Negro character in either of Kerouac's two novels is Mardou Fox, and she is about as primitive as Wilhelm Reich himself.

The plain truth is that the primitivism of the Beat Generation serves first of all as a cover for an anti-intellectualism so bitter that it makes the ordinary American's hatred of eggheads seem positively benign. Kerouac and his friends like to think of themselves as intellectuals ('they are intellectual as hell and know all about Pound without being pretentious or talking too much about it'), but this is only a form of newspeak. Here is an example of what Kerouac considers intelligent discourse —'formal and shining and complete, without the tedious intellectualness':

> We passed a little kid who was throwing stones at the cars in the road. 'Think of it,' said Dean. 'One day he'll put a stone through a man's windshield and the man will crash and die—all on account of that little kid. You see what I mean? God exists without qualms. As we roll along this way I am positive beyond doubt that everything will be taken care of for us—that even you, as you drive, fearful of the wheel . . . the thing will go along of itself and you won't go off the road and I can sleep. Furthermore we know America, we're at home; I can go anywhere in America and get what I want

because it's the same in every corner, I know the people, I know what they do. We give and take and go in the incredibly complicated sweetness zigzagging every side.'

You see what he means? Formal and shining and complete. No tedious intellectualness. Completely unpretentious. 'There was nothing clear about the things he said but what he meant to say was somehow made pure and clear.' *Somehow*. Of course. If what he wanted to say had been carefully thought out and precisely articulated, that would have been tedious and pretentious and, no doubt, *somehow* unclear and clearly impure. But so long as he utters these banalities with his tongue tied and with no comprehension of their meaning, so long as he makes noises that come out of his soul (since they couldn't possibly have come out of his mind), he passes the test of true intellectuality.

Which brings us to Kerouac's spontaneous bop prosody. This 'prosody' is not to be confused with bop language itself, which has such a limited vocabulary (Basic English is a verbal treasure-house by comparison) that you couldn't write a note to the milkman in it, much less a novel. Kerouac, however, manages to remain true to the spirit of hipster slang while making forays into enemy territory (i.e., the English language) by his simple inability to express anything in words. The only method he has of describing an object is to summon up the same half-dozen adjectives over and over again: 'greatest,' 'tremendous,' 'crazy,' 'mad,' 'wild,' and perhaps one or two others. When it's more than just mad or crazy or wild, it becomes 'really mad' or 'really crazy' or 'really wild.' (All quantities in excess of three, incidentally, are subsumed under the rubric 'innumerable,' a word used innumerable times in *On the Road* but not so innumerably in *The Subterraneans*.) The same poverty of resources is apparent in those passages where Kerouac tries to handle a situation involving even slightly complicated feelings. His usual tactic is to run for cover behind cliché and vague signals to the reader. For instance: 'I looked at him; my eyes were watering with embarrassment and tears. Still he stared

at me. Now his eyes were blank and looking through me. . . .
Something clicked in both of us. In me it was suddenly concern
for a man who was years younger than I, five years, and whose
fate was wound with mine across the passage of the recent
years; in him it was a matter that I can ascertain only from
what he did afterward.' If you can ascertain what this is all
about, either beforehand, during, or afterward, you are surely
no square.

In keeping with its populistic bias, the style of *On the Road*
is folksy and lyrical. The prose of *The Subterraneans*, on the
other hand, sounds like an inept parody of Faulkner at his
worst, the main difference being that Faulkner usually prod-
uces bad writing out of an impulse to inflate the commonplace
while Kerouac gets into trouble by pursuing 'spontaneity.'
Strictly speaking, spontaneity is a quality of feeling, not of
writing: when we call a piece of writing spontaneous, we are
registering our impression that the author hit upon the right
words without sweating, that no 'art' and no calculation entered
into the picture, that his feelings seem to have spoken themselves, seem to have sprouted a tongue at the moment of
composition. Kerouac apparently thinks that spontaneity is a
matter of saying whatever comes into your head, in any order
you happen to feel like saying it. It isn't the *right* words he
wants (even if he knows what they might be), but the first
words, or at any rate the words that most obviously announce
themselves as deriving from emotion rather than cerebration,
as coming from 'life' rather than 'literature,' from the guts
rather than the brain. (The brain, remember, is the angel of
death.) But writing that springs easily and 'spontaneously' out
of strong feelings is *never* vague; it always has a quality of
sharpness and precision because it is in the nature of strong
feelings to be aroused by specific objects. The notion that a
diffuse, generalized, and unrelenting enthusiasm is the mark
of great sensitivity and responsiveness is utterly fantastic, an
idea that comes from taking drunkenness or drug-addiction as
the state of perfect emotional vigor. The effect of such
enthusiasm is actually to wipe out the world altogether, for if
a filling station will serve as well as the Rocky Mountains to

arouse a sense of awe and wonder, then both the filling station and the mountains are robbed of their reality. Kerouac's conception of feeling is one that only a solipsist could believe in—and a solipsist, be it noted, is a man who does not relate to anything outside himself.

Solipsism is precisely what characterizes Kerouac's fiction. *On the Road* and *The Subterraneans* are so patently autobiographical in content that they become almost impossible to discuss as novels; if spontaneity were indeed a matter of destroying the distinction between life and literature, these books would unquestionably be It. 'As we were going out to the car Babe slipped and fell flat on her face. Poor girl was overwrought. Her brother Tim and I helped her up. We got in the car; Major and Betty joined us. The sad ride back to Denver began.' Babe is a girl who is mentioned a few times in the course of *On the Road;* we don't know why she is overwrought on this occasion, and even if we did it wouldn't matter, since there is no reason for her presence in the book at all. But Kerouac tells us that she fell flat on her face while walking toward a car. It is impossible to believe that Kerouac made this detail up, that his imagination was creating a world real enough to include wholly gratuitous elements; if that were the case, Babe would have come alive as a human being. But she is only a name; Kerouac never even describes her. She is in the book because the sister of one of Kerouac's friends was there when he took a trip to Central City, Colorado, and she slips in *On the Road* because she slipped that day on the way to the car. What is true of Babe who fell flat on her face is true of virtually every incident in *On the Road* and *The Subterraneans*. Nothing that happens has any dramatic reason for happening. Sal Paradise meets such-and-such people on the road whom he likes or (rarely) dislikes; they exchange a few words, they have a few beers together, they part. It is all very unremarkable and commonplace, but for Kerouac it is always the greatest, the wildest, the most. What you get in these two books is a man proclaiming that he is *alive* and offering every trivial experience he has ever had in evidence. Once I did this, once I did that (he is saying) and by God, it

meant something! Because I *responded*! But if it meant something, and you responded so powerfully, why can't you explain
what it meant, and why do you have to insist so?

I think it is legitimate to say, then, that the Beat Generation's
worship of primitivism and spontaneity is more than a cover
for hostility to intelligence; it arises from a pathetic poverty of
feeling as well. The hipsters and hipster-lovers of the Beat
Generation are rebels, all right, but not against anything so
sociological and historical as the middle class or capitalism
or even respectability. This is the revolt of the spiritually
underprivileged and the crippled of soul—young men who
can't think straight and so hate anyone who can; young men
who can't get outside the morass of self and so construct definitions of feeling that exclude all human beings who manage to
live, even miserably, in a world of objects; young men who
are burdened unto death with the specially poignant sexual
anxiety that America—in its eternal promise of erotic glory and
its spiteful withholding of actual erotic possibility—seems bent
on breeding, and who therefore dream of the unattainable
perfect orgasm, which excuses all sexual failures in the real
world. Not long ago, Norman Mailer suggested that the rise
of the hipster may represent 'the first wind of a second revolution in this century, moving not forward toward action and
more rational equitable distribution, but backward toward
being and the secrets of human energy.' To tell the truth,
whenever I hear anyone talking about instinct and being and
the secrets of human energy, I get nervous; next thing you
know he'll be saying that violence is just fine, and then I begin
wondering whether he really thinks that kicking someone in
the teeth or sticking a knife between his ribs are deeds to
be admired. History, after all—and especially the history of
modern times—teaches that there is a close connection between ideologies of primitivistic vitalism and a willingness to
look upon cruelty and blood-letting with complacency, if not
downright enthusiasm. The reason I bring this up is that the
spirit of hipsterism and the Beat Generation strikes me as the
same spirit which animates the young savages in leather jackets
who have been running amuck in the last few years with their

switch-blades and zip guns. What does Mailer think of those wretched kids, I wonder? What does he think of the gang that stoned a nine-year-old boy to death in Central Park in broad daylight a few months ago, or the one that set fire to an old man drowsing on a bench near the Brooklyn waterfront one summer's day, or the one that pounced on a crippled child and orgiastically stabbed him over and over and over again even after he was good and dead? Is that what he means by the liberation of instinct and the mysteries of being? Maybe so. At least he says somewhere in his article that two eighteen-year-old hoodlums who bash in the brains of a candy-store keeper are murdering an institution, committing an act that 'violates private property'—which is one of the most morally gruesome ideas I have ever come across, and which indicates where the ideology of hipsterism can lead. I happen to believe that there is a direct connection between the flabbiness of American middle-class life and the spread of juvenile crime in the 1950's, but I also believe that juvenile crime can be explained partly in terms of the same resentment against normal feeling and the attempt to cope with the world through intelligence that lies behind Kerouac and Ginsberg. Even the relatively mild ethos of Kerouac's books can spill over easily into brutality, for there is a suppressed cry in those books: Kill the intellectuals who can talk coherently, kill the people who can sit still for five minutes at a time, kill those incomprehensible characters who are capable of getting seriously involved with a woman, a job, a cause. How can anyone in his right mind pretend that this has anything to do with private property or the middle class? No. Being for or against what the Beat Generation stands for has to do with denying that incoherence is superior to precision; that ignorance is superior to knowledge; that the exercise of mind and discrimination is a form of death. It has to do with fighting the notion that sordid acts of violence are justifiable so long as they are committed in the name of 'instinct.' It even has to do with fighting the poisonous glorific-ation of the adolescent in American popular culture. It has to do, in other words, with being for or against intelligence itself.

JOYCE JOHNSON

'MEETS JOYCE GLASSMAN'*

As of 1982, there is the Jack Kerouac Society for Disembodied Poetics, founded in Boulder, Colorado, in 1976. There is *Jack's Book*, as well as *Desolation Angel: Jack Kerouac, the Beat Generation and America* and *Kerouac: A Biography* and—the one I like best—*Kerouac: A Chicken Essay*, by a French-Canadian surrealist poet; as well as proliferating pamphlets, theses, articles, chapters in books. A journal published annually celebrates the Beats and the 'Unspeakable Visions of the Individual.' It's hagiography in the making. Jack, now delivered into the Void, would be amazed to know there's even a literary fan magazine devoted entirely to him, called *Moody Street Irregulars* (after the street in Lowell where he lived as a child). For a back issue, a graduate student somewhere put together a rather randomly chosen chronology of Jack Kerouac's life. In a column labeled *1957*, there's a cryptic entry: *Meets Joyce Glassman*.

'Hello. I'm Jack. Allen tells me you're very nice. Would you like to come down to Howard Johnson's on Eighth Street? I'll be sitting at the counter. I have black hair and I'll be wearing a red and black checked shirt.'

I'm standing in Elise's kitchen, holding the phone Allen has just handed me. It's a Saturday night shortly after New Year's.

'Sure,' I say.

I put on a lot of eye shadow and my coat and take the subway down to Astor Place and begin walking westward, cross-town, passing under the bridge between the two buildings of Wanamaker's Department Store and the eye of the giant illuminated clock. It's a dark, bitter January night with ice all over the pavements, so you have to be careful, but I'm flying along, it's an adventure as opposed to a misadventure—under which

*From *Minor Characters*.

category so far I've had to put most of the risky occurrences in my life.

The windows of Howard Johnson's are running with steam so you can't see in. I push open the heavy glass door, and there is, sure enough, a black-haired man at the counter in a flannel lumberjack shirt slightly the worse for wear. He looks up and stares at me hard with blue eyes, amazingly blue. And the skin of his face is so brown. He's the only person in Howard Johnson's in color. I feel a little scared as I walk up to him. 'Jack?' I say.

There's an empty stool next to his. I sit down on it and he asks me whether I want anything. 'Just coffee.' He's awfully quiet. We both lack conversation, but then we don't know each other, so what can we say? He asks after Allen, Lafcadio, that kind of thing. I'd like to tell him I've read his book, if that wouldn't sound gauche, obvious and uncool.

When the coffee arrives, Jack looks glum. He can't pay for it. He has no money, none at all. That morning he'd handed his last ten dollars to a cashier in a grocery store and received change for a five. He's waiting for a check from a publisher, he says angrily.

I say, 'Look, that's all right. I have money. Do you want me to buy you something to eat?'

'Yeah,' he says. 'Frankfurters. I'll pay you back. I always pay people back, you know.'

I've never bought a man dinner before. It makes me feel very competent and womanly.

He has frankfurters, home fries, and baked beans with Heinz ketchup on them. I keep stealing looks at him because he's beautiful. You're not supposed to say a man is beautiful, but he is. He catches me at it and grins, then mugs it up, putting on one goofy face after another; a whole succession of old-time ridiculous movie-comedian faces flashes before me until I'm laughing too at the absurdity of this blind date Allen has arranged. (The notion of Allen Ginsberg arranging blind dates will crack people up years later when they ask me how on earth I met Kerouac.)

As for what he saw in me that night, I'm not sure at all. A

very young woman in a red coat, round-faced and blonde. 'An interesting young person,' he wrote in *Desolation Angels*. 'A Jewess, elegant middleclass sad and looking for something—she looked Polish as hell . . .' Where am I in all those funny categories?

As our paths converge in Howard Johnson's, we're looking for different things. At thirty-four, Jack's worn down, the energy that had moved him to so many different places gone. He's suddenly waited too long. The check for *The Subterraneans* will never arrive; *On the Road* will never be published. Why not let Allen rescue him? He can't go back to the two Virginias.

I see the blue, bruised eye of Kerouac and construe his melancholy as the look of a man needing love because I'm, among other things, twenty-one years old. I believe in the curative powers of love as the English believe in tea or Catholics believe in the Miracle of Lourdes.

He tells me he's spent sixty-three days on a mountaintop without anyone. He made pea soup and wrote in his journal and sang Sinatra songs to keep himself company.

Some warning to me in all this. 'You really liked being alone like that?' I ask.

'I wish I was there now. I should've stayed up there.'

He could somehow cancel you out and make you feel sad for him at the same time. But I'm sure any mountaintop would be preferable to where he's staying—the Marlton Hotel on Eighth Street, with the dirty shades over the windows and the winos lounging on the steps.

'And where do you live?' Jack asks. He likes it that it's up near Columbia and the West End Bar where he used to hang out. Was Johnny the bartender still there? Johnny the bartender would remember him from the days he was a football hero at Columbia but he broke his leg in his sophomore year and stayed in his room reading Céline and Shakespeare and never went back to football again—thus losing his scholarship at Columbia, but he's always had affection for the neighborhood. 'Why don't you let me stay at your place?' he says.

'If you wish,' I say in *Desolation Angels*, deciding fast. And

I know how I said it, too. As if it was of no great moment, as if I had no wishes of my own—in keeping with my current philosophy of nothing-to-lose, try anything.

We stood up and put on our coats, we went down into the subway. And there on the IRT, on a signboard I'd never seen before that night, was an ad for an airline with a brand-new slogan: FLY NOW. PAY LATER.

'That's a good title for a novel,' I said, and finally told Jack I was writing one, I wasn't just a secretary. He said *Pay Me the Penny After* would be a better title. 'You should call your novel that.' He asked me who my favorite writer was. I said Henry James, and he made a face, and said he figured I had all the wrong models, but maybe I could be a great writer anyway. He asked me if I rewrote a lot, and said you should never revise, never change anything, not even a word. He regretted all the rewriting he'd done on *The Town and the City*. No one could make him do that again, which was why he always got nowhere with publishers. He was going to look at my work and show me that what you wrote first was always best. I said okay, feeling guilty for all that I'd rewritten, but I still loved Henry James.

All through this literary conversation, Jack stood swaying above me on the subway, hanging on to the strap. Just before we got off, he leaned down. Our foreheads scraped, our eyeballs loomed up on each other—a funny game where I knew you weren't supposed to blink, no matter what.

That was the start of *Meets Joyce Glassman*.

The apartment I lived in at the time was dark and cavernous, on the first floor of a brownstone halfway down the block from the Yorkshire Hotel. Two furnished rooms—the furnishings being the uselessly massive, weak-jointed kind found in the lobbies of antediluvian apartment buildings. A small refrigerator and a two-burner stove stood behind a screen in one corner of the living room, but you had to wash your dishes in the bathroom sink. The windows looked out on a rank back yard where a large tree of heaven battened on bed-springs and broken bottles. I always felt very small in that apartment. One night outside the house a huge grey tomcat with a chewed ear had rubbed against my legs. I'd hauled him inside under the impression I was rescuing him, but he spent his days on the windowsill longing for the street, trying to pry the window open with his paw, or he lurked in the closet vengefully spraying shoes. Jack was the only person I'd brought home so far who saw the beauty of this animal, whom I'd unimaginatively named Smoke. He said he was going to call it Ti Gris, after a cat he once had in Lowell. He seemed to like to rename things. On the walk from the subway I'd become Joycey, which no one had called me since I was little, and he'd put his arm around me, leaning on me playfully and letting his hand dangle down over my breast—that was how men walked with their women in Mexico, he said. 'Someday when you go there, you'll see that for yourself.'

When we got in the door, he didn't ask to see my manuscript. He pulled me against him and kissed me before I even turned on the light. I kissed him back, and he acted surprised. He said I was even quieter than he was, he had no idea quiet girls liked kissing so much, and he undid the buttons of my coat and put both his hands up my back under my sweater. 'The trouble is,' Jack said with his voice against my ear, 'I don't . . . like . . . blondes.'

I remember laughing and saying, 'Well, in that case I'll just dye my hair'—wondering all the same if it was true.

In the morning Jack left to get his stuff out of the Marlton. He returned with a sleeping bag and a knapsack in which there were jeans and a few old shirts like the one he was already wearing and some notebooks he'd bought in Mexico City. That was all he owned. Not even a typewriter—he'd been borrowing other people's typewriters, he said. I'd never seen such foreign-looking notebooks, long and narrow with shiny black covers and thin, bluish paper on which Jack's slanted penciled printing sped across page after page, interrupted here and there by little sketches. One notebook was just for dreams. He wrote in it every morning.

There was something heartbreakingly attractive in these few

essentials to which Jack had reduced his needs. He reminded me of a sailor—not that I knew any sailors—something too about the way he looked coming out of the shower, gleaming and vigorous and ruddy with a white towel around his neck.

Very quickly it didn't seem strange to have him with me, we were somehow like very old friends—'buddies,' Jack said, squeezing me affectionately, making me feel both proud and a little disappointed. Crazy as it was, I sometimes really wished I was dark—like this Virginia I felt jealous of for making him so wild. Or the girl named Esmeralda who lived in Mexico City and whom he'd loved tragically for a long time and written an entire novel about in one of his notebooks, calling her Tristessa. But he'd slept with her only once. She was a whore and a saint, so beautiful and lost—one of his mysterious *fellaheen* women, primeval and of the earth.

I was unprimeval and distinctly of the city. I was everydayness, bacon and eggs in the morning or the middle of the night, which I learned to cook just the way he liked—sunny-side up in the black iron frying pan. I'd buy slab bacon in the grocery store, like he'd always had in Lowell—not the skinny kind in packages—and add canned apple-sauce (a refinement I'd learned from Bickford's Cafeteria), which Jack had never thought of as anything that might enhance eggs. He took extraordinary pleasure in small things like that.

As a lover he wasn't fierce but oddly brotherly and somewhat reticent. I'd listen in amazement to his stories of Berkeley parties where everyone was naked and men and women engaged in some exotic Japanese practice called *yabyum* (but Jack, fully clothed, had sat apart brooding over his bottle of port, something he didn't tell me). In my memories of Jack in the good times we had together, I'm lying with my head on his chest, his heart pulsing against my ear. His smooth hard powerful arms are around me and I'm burying my face into them because I like them so much, making him laugh, 'What are you doing there, Joycey?' And there's always music on the radio. Symphony Sid, whom he taught me to find on the dial, who always comes on at the stroke of midnight, bringing you the sounds of Charlie Parker, Lester Young, Miles Davis, and Stan Getz, and who, according to Jack, is a subterranean himself—you can hear it in his gravel voice smoked down to a rasp by innumerable weird cigarettes. 'And now—after a few words about that fan-tastic Mo-gen David wine—the great Lady Day . . .' In the darkness of the room we drift together as Billie Holiday bewails lost loves . . .

But then Jack leaves me. He goes into the small back bedroom where I never sleep because there's no radiator in there. He pulls the window all the way up, closes the door, and lies down on the floor in his sleeping bag alone. This is the cure for the cough he brought with him from Mexico City. In the morning he'll do headstands with his feet against the wall, to reverse the flow of blood in his body. He tells me a frightening thing about himself. He's known for eight years that a blood clot could finish him off at any minute.

How can you bear living, I wonder, knowing death could be so close? Little by little I'm letting go of what I learned on the abortionist's table in the white upstairs room in Canarsie.

I'm good for him, Jack tells me. I don't mind anything he does. I don't mind about the sleeping bag, do I?

I didn't really mind, that was the strange part. Everything seemed so odd, so charmed, so transformed. At night when the cold air came with a rush into the little room where Jack was sleeping, and seeped under the edges of the closed door, I could imagine myself in a place without walls, an immense campground where, lying wrapped in blankets, I could feel in my own warmth absolute proof of my existence.

I'm a regular fool in pale houses enslaved to lust for women who hate me, they lay their bartering flesh all over the divans, it's one fleshpot—insanity all of it, I should forswear and chew em all out and go hit the clean rail—I wake up glad to find myself saved in the wilderness mountains—For that lumpy roll flesh with the juicy hole I'd sit through eternities of horror in gray rooms illuminated by a gray sun, with cops and alimoners at the door and the jail beyond?—It's a bleeding comedy—The Great Wise Stages of pathetic

understanding elude me when it comes to harems—
Harem-scarem, it's all in heaven now—bless their all
their bleating-hearts—Some lambs are female, some
angels have womanwings, it's all mothers in the end
and forgive me for my sardony—excuse me for my rut.
(Hor hor hor)

Not for Joyce Glassman to read, this bleak passage later
written in *Desolation Angels*, this awful metaphysical linking
of sex, birth, the grave. I hate Jack's woman-hatred, hate it,
mourn it, understand, and finally forgive.

BIOGRAPHICAL NOTES

NELSON ALGREN (1909–1981) was born in Detroit and grew up in the Chicago slums. His literary career began with *Somebody in Boots* (1935), an account of a poor-white Texas boy's experience as a vagabond and criminal during the Depression. Other novels include, *Never Come Morning* (1942); *The Man With the Golden Arm* (1949) and *A Walk on the Wild Side* (1956). Among his stories and travel reports are *The Neon Wilderness* (1947); *Who Lost an American?* (1963) and *The Last Carousel* (1973). *Notes from a Sea Diary* (1965) is a collection of short stories and a commentary on the writer Ernest Hemingway. He taught a writing course at Chicago University in 1950–51; his love-affair with Simone de Beauvoir is recalled in her autobiography *La Force des Choses* (*Force of Circumstances*) in 1963.

WILLIAM BURROUGHS (1914– 1997) was born in St Louis, graduated at Harvard and has spent long periods of his life living abroad in Paris and Tangiers. He has worked as a private detective, exterminator, film actor and bartender. He is best known for his frank accounts of his life as a drug addict in *Junkie* (1953, published under the pseudonym, William Lee) and *The Naked Lunch* (1959, 1962). Other works related to the Beat movement include *The Exterminator* (1960); *The Soft Machine* (1961); *Nova Express* (1964), a satire on modern life; *Wild Boys* (1971); a fantasy about revolutionary homosexuals and *Cities of the Red Night* (1981). *The Yage Letters* (1963) is a collection of correspondence with Allen Ginsberg. His most recent work is *The Place of Dead Roads* (1984).

GREGORY CORSO (1930–   ) was born in New York City and spent three years in Clinton State Prison. His volumes of poetry *Bomb* (1958) and *Gasoline* (1958) were produced by City Lights Press, Lawrence Ferlinghetti's publishing house. Later he lived with Ginsberg and the poet Orlovsky in Paris until 1961. His collections of poetry include *The Vestal Lady of Brattle* (1955); *The Happy Birthday of Death* (1960) and *Elegiac*

Feelings American (1970). He has also written a play, *This Hung-up Age* (1955) and a novel, *The American Express* (1961) and has taught at the State University of New York at Buffalo.

LAWRENCE FERLINGHETTI (1920–   ) was born in New York and attended Columbia University and the University of Paris. He published Allen Ginsberg's *Howl and Other Poems* (1956) at the City Lights Press as well as Corso's *Gasoline* (1958), Kerouac's *Book of Dreams* (1960) and works by Charles Bukowski and Sam Shepard. His City Lights Bookstore in San Francisco was a centre for many writers and artists of the Beat movement. His own works include *Pictures of the Gone World* (1955); *A Coney Island of the Mind* (1958); *The Secret Meaning of Things* (1969) and *Endless Life* (1981). He has also written a novel, a pictorial history of San Francisco and some experimental plays.

ALLEN GINSBERG (1926–*1997*) was born in Newark, New Jersey, and graduated from Columbia University. In 1955 he joined the Beat movement in San Francisco and found fame with his first collection of verse, *Howl and Other Poems* (1956), whose publisher, fellow-poet Lawrence Ferlinghetti was tried and acquitted in court for issuing an allegedly obscene work. His reputation as a passionate, outspoken writer was enhanced by *Kaddish and Other Poems* (1961), whose title work was a lyrical lament for his recently dead mother. Later publications include *Reality Sandwiches* (1963); *The Fall of America: Poems of These States* (1973); *First Blues* (1975) and *Plutonian Ode* (1981). He was granted a National Book Award for *The Fall of America* in 1973. Among his volumes of prose are *The Yage Letters* (1963); *Indian Journals* (1970) and *As Ever* (1977), a collection of the correspondence of Neal Cassady. He has travelled extensively to Cuba, India, Japan, the U.S.S.R. and Eastern Europe and is widely recognised for his anti-authoritarian views and for his pacifist idea of 'flower power', a phrase he coined. His *Collected Poems* were published in 1985.

JOHN CLELLON HOLMES (1926–   ) was born in Holyoke, Massachusetts. He served in the Navy in World War II and studied at Columbia University and The New School for Social

Research. He has written and published poetry, but is best known for his novels: *Go* (1952), *The Horn* (1958) and *Get Home Free* (1964). His autobiographical *Nothing More to Declare* (1967) looks back at the Beat writers. In conversation he heard Jack Kerouac use the term 'beat generation', and then introduced that phrase to the public himself in 'This is the Beat Generation', an article in *The New York Times* in 1952.

JOYCE JOHNSON, as Joyce Glassman, a young Barnard College student who had been raised at West 116th Street in New York, met Jack Kerouac on a blind date arranged by Allen Ginsberg in 1957. Her excellent account of their subsequent relationship is found in her work, *Minor Characters* (1983). She is also the author of two novels, *Bad Connections* and *Come and Join the Dance*. She is now an executive editor at Dial Press and lives in New York City.

LEROI JONES (1934–   ) was born in New Jersey and educated at Howard University and Columbia. He was co-editor and music editor on *Yugen* and *Kulchur* magazines but later rejected the Beat movement and took the name Imamu Amiri Baraka as part of his commitment to Afro-Americanism. His poems include *Preface to a Twenty Volume Suicide Note* (1961); *Black Magic* (1969) and *In Our Terribleness* (1971). His greatest distinction is as a playwright, and his stark, lean, sharp, semi-naturalistic plays include *The Dutchman* (1974), later made into a film. Among his non-fiction works are *Blues People* (1963); *Black Art* (1967) and *African Revolution* (1973). His *Selected Plays and Prose* and *Selected Poems* were both published in 1979. He lives and works in Newark, New Jersey.

JACK KEROUAC (1922–1969), born Jean Louis Lebris de Kerouac in Lowell, Massachusetts, of French-Canadian descent, spoke French in early childhood before he learned English. After a year at Horace Mann High School in the Bronx, he entered Columbia University on a football scholarship, quit, re-enrolled later, but never took a degree. His most famous work, *On the Road* (1957) is a quasi-autobiographical account of his travels with his friend Neal Cassady of Denver. Other writings include *The Town and City* (1950) published on the recommendation of his Columbia professor, Mark Van Doren; *The Dharma Bums* (1958), in which he and Ginsberg appear as Ray Smith and Alvah Goldbook exploring Buddhism; *The Subterraneans* (1958); *Doctor Sax* (1959); *Big Sur* (1962), an account of his retreat from fame to Ferlinghetti's borrowed cottage; and *Desolation Angels* (1965). His *Mexico City Blues* (1959) is a volume of poetry; his travel writings are collected in *Lonesome Traveller* (1960), *Satori in Paris* (1960) and *Visions of Cody* (1960), recollections of travels with Cassady. A long-time alcoholic, Kerouac died at the early age of 47 in Florida. Beat writers of the 1950s acknowledge his influence, and he is the most important novelist among the 'Beat generation'.

SEYMOUR KRIM has written for various newspapers and magazines including *The Washington Post*, *New York Times Book Review*, *Village Voice*, *Partisan Review* and *Commentary*. His anthology, *The Beats* (1960) established him as an authority on the Beat movement. He teaches at Columbia University and lives in New York.

TULI KUPFERBERG is a writer, poet and publisher who now lives in Greenwich Village. He is the author of some 20 books including *1001 Ways to Beat the Draft*, *1001 Ways to Live Without Working* and *1001 Ways to Make Love*. He was founder and songwriter of the satirical rock group, 'The Fugs' and is currently director of the Revolving Theatre and a singing cartoonist.

PHILIP LAMANTIA (1927–   ) was already well established as a Surrealist poet when he became part of the Beat movement. In the 1940s he worked with Charles Henri Ford on *View*, an influential surrealist magazine. His works include *Erotic Poems* (1946); *Ekstasis* (1959); *The Blood of the Air* (1970) and *Becoming Visible* (1981). He features as the character Francis DePavia in Jack Kerouac's *The Dharma Bums*.

NORMAN PODHORETZ (1930–   ) was born in Brooklyn and studied at Columbia University and Clare College, Cambridge. His sociocultural essays are collected in *Doings and Undoings: The Fifties and After in American Writing* (1964). Other works include *Making It* (1967), an account of a writer's efforts to succeed in the New York intellectual society; *Breaking Ranks* (1979), a candid memoir of political issues, and *Why We Were in Vietnam* (1982). He became editor of *Commentary* magazine in 1960, a position he still holds.

DAN PROPPER grew up and was educated in Brooklyn and now lives in California. He first received recognition as a poet with his poem 'The Fable of the Final Hour' and later took part in jazz readings with Dizzy Gillespie and Thelonius Monk. His work, *For Kerouac in Heaven*, was published in 1980.

KENNETH REXROTH (1905–1982) was born in Indiana and lived in San Francisco. He was a poet, painter, dramatist, critic and translator and published over 20 books in his lifetime. His collections of poems include, *The Phoenix and the Tortoise* (1944), *In Defence of the Earth* (1956) and *New Poems* (1974). Among his volumes of essays are *Bird in the Bush* (1959) and *The Elastic Retort* (1974). Rexroth organised the reading, 'Six Poets at the Six Gallery', in San Francisco in October 1955, where Ginsberg famously read 'Howl'.

GARY SNYDER (1930–   ) was born in San Francisco but grew up on a farm in Washington and Portland. He studied Oriental languages at the University of California. He later became a tanker seaman and in 1956 travelled to Japan to study Zen Buddhism. Among his volumes of poetry are *Riprap* (1959); *Six Sections from Mountains and Rivers Without End (1965, 1970)*; *Regarding Wave* (1970) and the Pulitzer Prize-winning *Turtle Island* (1974). *Earth House Hold* (1969) and *The Old Ways* (1977) are collections of essays. Snyder features as Japhy Ryder in Kerouac's *Dharma Bums*. He now lives with his Japanese wife on a farm in California.

SALLY STERN, despite Paul O'Neill's statement in 'The Only Rebellion Around', in *Life* magazine, 30 November 1959, that there could be 'few female Beats', is one of the talented poets of the 1950s who expressed the Beat outlook in her verse. The anthologised poem is taken from *The Beat Scene*, edited by Elias Wilentz, Corinth Books, 1960.

DIANA TRILLING (1905–   ) is an essayist on literary, social and political subjects. Her works include *Claremont Essays* (1964); *We Must March My Darlings: A Critical Decade* (1977); *Reviewing the Forties* (1978) and *Mrs Harris—The Death of the Scarsdale Diet Doctor* (1981). She is a contributor to *Partisan Review, Harper's, Vanity Fair* and *The Times* among other journals, and she was married to the writer and lecturer, Lionel Trilling. Despite reservations, she took a more sympathetically perceptive view of Allen Ginsberg's poetry than Trilling, Auden and their friends did in the 1950s.

FURTHER READING

ALLEN, DONALD M. and TALLMAN, WARREN, eds., *Poetics of the New American Poetry* (New York: Grove Press, 1974).

AMBROSE, STEPHEN E., *Eisenhower*, 2 vols. (London: George Allen & Unwin, 1984).

BARTLETT, LEE, ed., *The Beats: Essays in Criticism* (Jefferson, North Carolina: McFarland, 1981).

BEAULIEU, VICTOR-LÉVY, *Jack Kerouac: A Chicken-Essay* (Toronto: Coach House Press, 1975).

CHARTERS, ANN, *Beats & Company: Portrait of a Literary Generation* (New York: Doubleday, 1986).

COOK, BRUCE, *The Beat Generation* (New York: Scribner's, 1971).

DIPRIMA, DIANE, *Memoirs of a Beatnik* (New York: Olympia, 1969).

FASS, EKBERT, *Towards a New American Poetics: Essays and Interviews* (Santa Barbara, Calif.: Black Sparrow Press, 1979).

FELDMAN, GENE, and GARTENBERG, MAX, eds., *The Beat Generation and the Angry Young Men* (New York: Citadel Press, 1958, and repr. Dell, 1959).

FERLINGHETTI, LAWRENCE, ed., *Beatitude Anthology* (San Francisco: City Lights Books, 1969).

GINSBERG, ALLEN, *The Visions of the Great Remember* (Amherst, Mass.: Mulch Press, 1974).

——, *Allen Verbatim: Lectures on Poetry, Politics, Consciousness*, ed. Gordon Ball (London and New York: McGraw–Hill, 1974).

HIPKISS, ROBERT A., *Jack Kerouac: Prophet of the New Romanticism* (Lawrence, Kansas: Regents Press, 1976).

HOLMES, JOHN CLELLON, *Nothing More to Declare* (New York: Dutton, 1967).

HUNT, TIM, *Kerouac's Crooked Road: Development of a Fiction* (Hamden, Conn.: Archon, 1981).

JOHNSON, JOYCE, *Minor Characters* (London: Picador, Pan Books and William Collins Sons, 1983).

KAZIN, ALFRED, introd., *Writers at Work: The Paris Review*

Interviews, Third Series (London: Secker & Warburg, 1967)—'Burroughs', 'Ginsberg'.

KRIM, SEYMOUR, ed., *The Beats* (Simon & Schuster Inc., 1960).

LIPTON, LAWRENCE, *The Holy Barbarians* (New York: Messner, 1959).

MCDARRAH, FRED W., *Kerouac and Friends: A Beat Generation Album* (New York: William Morrow, 1985).

MCNALY, DENNIS, *Desolate Angel: Jack Kerouac, the Beats & America* (New York: Random House, 1979).

NICOSIA, GERALD, *Memory Babe: A Critical Biography of Jack Kerouac* (New York: Grove Press, 1983).

PARKINSON, THOMAS, ed., *A Casebook on the Beat* (New York: Thomas Y. Crowell Co., 1961).

TYTELL, JOHN, *Naked Angels: The Lives and Literature of the Beat Generation* (New York: McGraw-Hill, 1977).

WILENTZ, ELIAS, ed., *The Beat Scene* (New York: Corinth Books, 1960).

LIST OF SOURCES

Poetry ·

Allen Ginsberg, 'A Supermarket in California': *Howl and Other Poems*, 1956; 'The Lion for Real', 'Death to Van Gogh's Ear, 'Mescaline': *Kaddish and Other Poems*, 1961; 'Under the World There's a Lot of Ass, A Lot of Cunt': *Mindbreaths*, 1978; 'The Green Automobile': *Reality Sandwiches*, 1963; 'Paterson': *Empty Mirror*, 1961.

Gregory Corso, 'The Thin Thin Line', 'Writ on the Steps of Puerto Rican Harlem' and 'Horses': *Long Live Man*, 1962: 'Marriage': *The Happy Birthday of Death*, 1960; 'Ode to Old England and Its Language' and 'America Politica Historia, in Spontaneity': *Elegiac Feelings American*, 1970; 'Columbia U Poesy Reading—1975': *Herald of the Autochthonic Spirit*, 1980.

Lawrence Ferlinghetti, 'Autobiography', 'I Have Not Lain With Beauty All My Life . . .', 'The Poet's Eye Obscenely Seeing . . .': *A Coney Island of the Mind*, 1958; 'Underwear': *Starting from San Francisco*, 1961; 'Adieu à Charlot': *Landscapes of Living and Dying*, 1979.

Gary Snyder, all poems: *Riprap*, 1959.

Philip Lamantia, 'Fud at Foster's'; Tuli Kupferberg, 'Greenwich Village of My Dreams'; Sally Stern, 'Wait, I've Been This Way Before'; Dan Propper, 'Afternoon'; Le Roi Jones, 'Epistrophe': *The Beat Scene*, ed. Elias Wilentz, 1960.

Prose and Commentary
Allen Ginsberg, *Journals*, 1957.
Jack Kerouac, '110 mph and The American Bop Night': *On the Road*, 1957; 'Zen': *The Dharma Bums*, 1958.
'William Lee' (William Burroughs), 'My First Days on Junk': *Junkie*, 1953. John Clellon Holmes, 'Go':, *Go* 1952.

Seymour Krim, 'The Insanity Bit': *Exodus Magazine*, 1959.

John Clellon Holmes, 'The Philosophy of the Beat Generation', *Esquire*, 1958.

Diana Trilling, 'The Other Night at Columbia', *Partisan Review*, Spring 1959 (revised) *Claremont Essays*, 1964.

Allen Ginsberg, '*Paris Review* Interview', 1965.

Allen Ginsberg, 'Kerouac': *Allen Verbatim*, ed. G. Bell, 1974.

Park Honan, 'A Beat Precursor: Nelson Algren': *New City* (Chicago), January 1964.

Kenneth Rexroth, 'Disengagement: The Art of the Beat Generation': *New World Writing* No. 11, 1957.

Norman Podhoretz, 'The Know-Nothing Bohemians', *Partisan Review*, 1958.

Joyce Johnson, 'Meets Joyce Glassman': *Minor Characters*, 1983.

ACKNOWLEDGEMENTS

Acknowledgements are due to the following for permission to include material which appears in this book:

Penguin Books Ltd. for the poems from Allen Ginsberg: *The Collected Poems 1947–1980* (Viking Books 1985); poems by Allen Ginsberg © Allen Ginsberg 1985. Pan Books for 'Meets Joyce Glassman' from Joyce Johnson: *Minor Characters* (Pan Books, 1983); 'Meets Joyce Glassman' © Joyce Johnson 1983. Diana Trilling for 'The Other Night at Columbia', *Partisan Review* 1959; *Claremont Essays*, Harcourt Brace and World, 1964; Secker & Warburg, 1965; 'The Other Night at Columbia' © Diana Trilling 1959. The Sterling Lord Agency, Inc. for 'Epistrophe (for Yodo)' by LeRoi Jones from *The Beat Scene*, ed. Elias Wilentz (Corinth Books, 1960); 'Epistrophe (for Yodo)' © LeRoi Jones 1960. Seymour Krim for 'The Insanity Bit' from *Exodus Magazine*, 1959; 'The Insanity Bit' © Seymour Krim 1959. Tuli Kupferberg for 'Greenwich Village of My Dreams' from *The Beat Scene* ed. Elias Wilentz (Corinth Books 1960); 'Greenwich Village of My Dreams' © Tuli Kupferberg 1960. Richard Scott Simon Ltd. for Norman Podhoretz: 'The Know-Nothing Bohemians' from *The Beats* ed. Seymour Krim (Simon & Schuster Inc. 1960); 'The Know-Nothing Bohemians' © Norman Podhoretz 1958. Laurence Pollinger Ltd. and New Directions for poems by Lawrence Ferlinghetti, Gregory Corso and Gary Snyder; Poems by Lawrence Ferlinghetti © Lawrence Ferlinghetti 1958, 1961, 1979; Poems by Gregory Corso © Gregory Corso 1960, 1962, 1970, 1975; Poems by Gary Snyder © Gary Snyder 1959. Laurence Pollinger Ltd. and Kenneth Rexroth for 'Disengagement: The Art of the Beat Generation' from *New World Writing, No. 11, 1957*; 'Disengagement: The Art of the Beat Generation' © Kenneth Rexroth 1957. Philip Lamantia for 'Fud at Foster's' from *The Beat Scene* ed. Elias Wilentz (Corinth Books, 1960); 'Fud at Foster's' © Philip Lamantia 1960. Sally Stern for 'Wait, I've Been This Way Before' from *The Beat Scene* ed. Elias Wilentz (Corinth Books, 1960); 'Wait, I've Been This Way Before' © Sally Stern 1960. Dan Propper for 'Afternoon' from *The Beat Scene* ed. Elias Wilentz (Corinth Books, 1960) 'Afternoon' © Dan Propper 1960. Andre Deutsch Ltd. for '110 Mph and The American Bop Night' from Jack Kerouac: *On the Road* (Andre Deutsch, 1957) and 'Zen' from Jack Kerouac: *The Dharma Bums* (Andre Deutsch, 1958); '110 Mph and the American Bop Night' © Jack Kerouac 1957; 'Zen' © Jack Kerouac 1958. A. D. Peters & Co Ltd. for 'My First Days on Junk' from William Burroughs ('William Lee'): *Junkie* (Ace Books, 1953); 'My First Days on Junk' © William Burroughs 1953. The Sterling Lord Agency, Inc. for 'Go' from John Clellon Holmes: *Go* (E. P. Dutton, 1952) and 'The Philosophy of the Beat Generation' from *Esquire*, 1958 and *Nothing More to Declare 1963 – 1967* (E. P. Dutton); 'Go' © John Clellon Holmes 1952, 1980, 'The Philosophy of the Beat Generation' © John Clellon Holmes 1958. Lawrence A. Ragan for Park Honan: 'A Beat Precursor: Nelson Algren' from 'Nelson Algren Came Down Division Street' from *New City*, (Chicago January 1964) 'A Beat Precursor: Nelson Algren' © Park Honan 1964. Aitken Stone Ltd. for Allen Ginsberg: 'Kerouac' from *Allen Verbatim* (McGraw Hill 1974), 'Interview' from *Paris Review*, 1965 and *Journals*, 1957; Prose by Allen Ginsberg © 1957, 1965, 1974.

For help of various kinds, the editor thanks W. H. Honan of *The New York Times*, as well as Brian Harding, Richard B. Hovey and Robyn Sisman.

AHARON APPELFELD
Badenheim 1939

A haunting novel set in 1939 in a picturesque Austrian resort-town, where the Jewish holiday-makers passively await their fate. 'An extraordinarily beautiful and sad book'. *TLS*

J. G. BALLARD
The Drowned World

Ballard's classic novel, set in a tropical, flooded London of the near future, is a fast-paced narrative full of stunning images that reflect on our own society. 'This tale of strange and terrible adventure in a world of steaming jungles has an oppressive power reminiscent of Conrad.' *Kingsley Amis*

J. G. BALLARD
The Terminal Beach

This brilliant collection of stories ranges from a disturbing picture of an abandoned atomic testing island in the Pacific to the shocking Oedipal fantasy of 'The Gioconda of the Twilight Noon'.

J. G. BALLARD
Vermilion Sands

Vermilion Sands is J. G. Ballard's fantasy landscape of the near future, where he would be happy to live himself – a latterday Palm Springs populated by forgotten movie queens, temperamental dilettantes and drugged beachcombers, with prima donna plants that sing arias, cloud sculptures, dial-a-poem computers and ravishing, jewel-eyed Jezebels.

J. G. BALLARD
The Voices of Time

Ballard's extraordinary inventiveness and the unfailing grace and energy of his writing are triumphantly on display in this classic collection of stories, which includes 'The Overloaded Man', 'Chronopolis', and 'The Garden of Time', which Anthony Burgess has called 'one of the most beautiful stories of the world canon of short fiction'.

The Best of Fiction Magazine
Edited by JUDY COOKE

A varied and entertaining selection of new writing published in *The Fiction Magazine* since its launch in 1982. Here are stories, poems and essays by Deborah Moggach, Anthony Burgess, Simon Burt, Marina Warner, Brian Aldiss, John McGahern and many others.

RACHEL INGALLS
Binstead's Safari

A love story with a fantastical twist, in which an unremarkable American couple are transformed by their experiences in the lion country of East Africa. Witty, entertaining, beautifully written, '*Binstead's Safari* is a small triumph . . . It should, if there is any justice, bring Rachel Ingalls hundreds of new admirers' Paul Bailey, *The Standard*

RACHEL INGALLS
Mrs Caliban and Others

In these three short novels Rachel Ingalls blends fantasy and legend with the deftly captured details of everyday life to explore the effects — sometimes bizarre, sometimes tragic — of isolation. *Mrs Caliban* was chosen as one of the top twenty post-war American novels for the Book Marketing Council's 'Books USA' campaign.

Interzone: The 1st Anthology
Edited by JOHN CLUTE, COLIN GREENLAND and DAVID PRINGLE

This anthology presents the best new writing in science fiction and fantasy today, by talented newcomers as well as by established writers such as J. G. Ballard, Angela Carter and Keith Roberts. 'An exceptional anthology ... it should not be missed.' *City Limits*

JAMES KELMAN
The Busconductor Hines

An intelligent, funny and astonishingly original novel that offers a brilliantly executed, uncompromising slice of working-class Glasgow life. 'James Kelman is masterly ... *The Busconductor Hines* is the only work of realistic literary art to show what is happening to most of the British people here and now.' *Alasdair Gray*

The Best of Ring Lardner
Chosen and introduced by DAVID LODGE

Ring Lardner was one of America's great satirists — funny, acute, wholly original. These stories are vivid verbal snapshots of 1920s America, with its baseball players and commercial travellers, Broadway impresarios and small-town barbers, flappers and gold-diggers, hen-pecked husbands and bridge-playing wives. 'Highly enjoyable.' *Anthony Burgess*; 'A superb collection of the great American satirist's work. A nugget.' *Time Out*

JOYCE CAROL OATES
Unholy Loves

A famous but deplorably behaved English poet visits an East Coast university in this witty and wickedly perceptive campus novel by one of America's most highly regarded writers. 'Immensely entertaining stuff ... snide and rueful by turn' *Elizabeth Berridge, Daily Telegraph*

JOYCE CAROL OATES
Wild Saturday and Other Stories

Often compared to Carson McCullers and Flannery O'Connor, Joyce Carol Oates is perhaps at her very best in the short story. These vivid, often disturbing stories chronicle the lives of young Americans searching for identity in a socially and morally lawless age, who become casualties of their own rebellion. 'A rare treat.' *Time Out*

JOSÉ CARDOSO PIRES
Ballad of Dogs' Beach
Translated from the Portuguese by MARY FITTON

In his powerful novel based on a true series of events in Salazar's Portugal in 1960, the author has drawn upon secret police files to give a highly dramatic account of a political murder. 'The author's real talents lie in his exposure of the intrinsic allure at the heart of the banal apparatus of dictatorship.' *Jonathan Keates, The Observer*

The Secret Self: Short Stories by Women
Selected and Introduced by HERMIONE LEE

A superb collection of short stories written in English by women during the 20th century, from Katherine Mansfield and Willa Cather to Angela Carter and Margaret Atwood. 'A totally successful book.' *Harriett Gilbert, New Statesman*; '*The Secret Self* is a triumph.' *Women's Review*

IGNAZIO SILONE
Fontamara
Introduction by MICHAEL FOOT
Translated from the Italian by ERIC MOSBACHER

Set in the 1930s in Italy, '*Fontamara* is the most moving account of Fascist barbarity ... It should be read to its merciless end.' *Graham Greene*

IGNAZIO SILONE
Bread and Wine
Translated from the Italian by ERIC MOSBACHER

Bread and Wine tells the story of the clandestine homecoming to Italy during the Fascist regime of a revolutionary who disguises himself as a priest to avoid capture. 'The book's idealism and symbolism are still potent today.' *Peter Allen, Western Morning News*

ELLEASE SOUTHERLAND
Let the Lion Eat Straw

A moving and triumphant novel about Abeba Williams Lavoisier, born poor, black and illegitimate in America's rural South. 'This book is a miracle . . . As a debut it is astounding; as an achievement it is even more so' *Bernard Levin, Sunday Times*

DYLAN THOMAS
The Collected Stories
Foreword by Leslie Norris

This collected edition of stories by one of the great twentieth-century poets and writers reveals Dylan Thomas in all his intriguing diversity — as sombre fantasist, exuberant word-spinner and comedian of suburban Swansea. 'Here are the unself-conscious classics, compassionate, fresh and very funny . . . radiating enthusiasm and delight in the telling' *New Statesman*

DYLAN THOMAS
Portrait of the Artist as a Young Dog

Dylan Thomas's classic book, based on his youth in suburban Swansea — lyrical, rumbustious, brimming with life. 'Fresh and amusing as ever' *Eastern Daily Press*

FRANCES THOMAS
Seeing Things

A deliciously sharp comedy sparked off by an Irish schoolgirl's vision of the Virgin Mary on a South London common. 'A first novel of tremendous style and verve' *Susan Hill*; 'Masterly . . . I'd put it straight in the Alice Thomas Ellis class' *Books and Bookmen*

ZDENA TOMIN
Stalin's Shoe

A wonderfully fresh and unusual novel by an exiled Czech writer, which offers a haunting portrait of Prague after World War II as well as a moving exploration of a lonely woman's struggle to come to terms with her past and herself. 'Brilliant' *Fay Weldon*; 'good enough to suggest that she could join that line of Eastern Europeans — Conrad, Nabokov, Koestler — who have enriched English Literature' *Allan Massie, Scotsman*

TENNESSEE WILLIAMS
Three Players of a Summer Game and Other Stories

An electrifying collection of Williams's best stories, written at the height of his creative power.

WILLIAM WOODRUFF
Vessel of Sadness

A rediscovered classic of war literature, distilled from the author's experience as a British infantryman fighting at Anzio in World War II. 'I've never read a better book about war; a book so humane, so wretched . . .' *John Milne, Time Out*

Further details about Everyman Fiction, and about all Dent Paperbacks, including Everyman Classics and Classic Thrillers, may be obtained from the Sales Department, J. M. Dent & Sons Ltd, 33 Welbeck Street, London W1M 8LX.

ORDER FORM

....	APPELFELD: Badenheim 1939	£2.95
....	BALLARD: The Drowned World	£2.50
....	BALLARD: The Terminal Beach	£2.95
....	BALLARD: Vermilion Sands	£2.95
....	BALLARD: The Voices of Time	£2.95
....	THE BEATS: (ed.) Park Honan	£4.95
....	BEST OF FICTION MAGAZINE: (ed.) Judy Cooke	£4.95
....	FLEETWOOD: An Artist and a Magician	£2.95
....	FLEETWOOD: The Order of Death	£2.95
....	INGALLS: Binstead's Safari	£2.95
....	INGALLS: Mrs Caliban and Others	£2.95
....	INTERZONE: The 1st Anthology	£3.95
....	KELMAN: The Busconductor Hines	£2.95
....	LEE (ed.): The Secret Self: Short Stories by Women	£3.95
....	LODGE (ed.): The Best of Ring Lardner	£2.95
....	NORMAN: Wild Thing	£2.95
....	OATES: Wild Saturday and Other Stories	£2.95
....	OATES: Unholy Loves	£3.50
....	PIRES: Ballad of Dogs' Beach	£4.50
....	DE SENA: The Wondrous Physician	£3.95
....	SILONE: Fontamara	£4.50
....	SILONE: Bread and Wine	£4.95
....	SOUTHERLAND: Let the Lion Eat Straw	£2.95
....	STOW: The Suburbs of Hell	£2.95
....	THOMAS: The Collected Stories	£3.50
....	THOMAS: Portrait of the Artist as a Young Dog	£2.25
....	THOMAS: Seeing Things	£3.95
....	TOMIN: Stalin's Shoe	£3.95
....	WILLIAMS: Three Players of a Summer Game and Other Stories	£2.95
....	WOODRUFF: Vessel of Sadness	£2.95

All these books may be obtained through your local bookshop, or can be ordered direct from the publisher. Please indicate the number of copies required and fill in the form below.

Name .... BLOCK

Address .... LETTERS

.... PLEASE

Please enclose remittance to the value of the cover price *plus* 40p per copy to a maximum of £2, for postage, and send your order to: BP Dept, J.M. Dent & Sons Ltd, 33 Welbeck Street, London W1M 8LX
Applicable to UK only and subject to stock availability
All prices subject to alteration without notice